Treasures from the Cairo Museum

Treasures of Egyptian Art from the Cairo Museum

EDWARD L. B. TERRACE AND HENRY G. FISCHER

A Centennial Exhibition 1970-71

Museum of Fine Arts, Boston
and The Metropolitan Museum of Art
in conjunction with Los Angeles County Museum of Art

LIBRARY OF CONGRESS CATALOG CARD NUMBER: 78–117507

THIS CATALOGUE HAS BEEN DESIGNED AND PRODUCED
BY THAMES AND HUDSON LIMITED

FILMSET IN GREAT BRITAIN BY KEYSPOOLS LIMITED, GOLBORNE, LANCS
PRINTED BY CONZETT AND HUBER, ZURICH, SWITZERLAND
BOUND BY VAN RIJMENAM N.V., THE HAGUE, HOLLAND

CONTENTS

I Chephren, the Living Horus

following pages

II Jewellery of the Princess Khnumet

III Seneb and his family

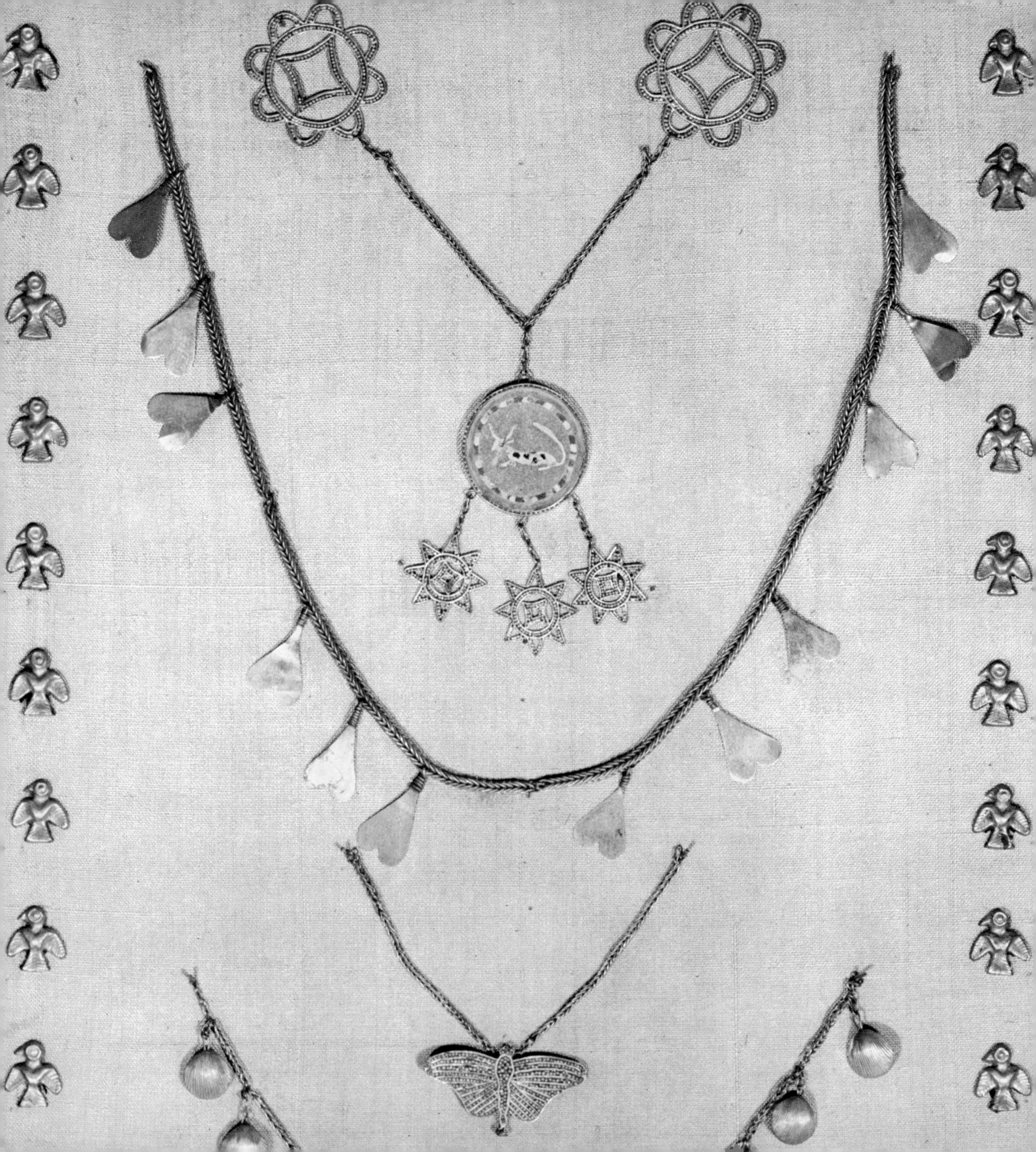

FOREWORD

DR SARWAT OKASHA

Minister of Culture
Cairo, U.A.R.

The famous collections of Egyptian art in the Boston and The Metropolitan Museums are permanent representatives abroad of the countless treasures to be seen today in the United Arab Republic. Now, on the occasion of the centennial celebrations of these two museums, the Ministry of Culture is happy to send temporary ambassadors to join their expatriate brothers. A selection of some of the most important pieces has been made from the unparalleled riches of the Egyptian Museum in Cairo, including what many believe to be the most beautiful ancient Egyptian sculpture in the world, the magnificent statue of Chephren. Because sculpture is the art *par excellence* of pharaonic Egypt, the exhibition is made up almost entirely of this form, and examples have been chosen from every great period ranging from the archaic beginnings to the end with the porphyry bust of a late Roman Emperor which heralds the beginnings of medieval art.

Art, like music, knows no boundaries, and it is a truly international means of communication. In a world of change and conflict, art is a reality: basic and immutable. Here man may find his true goodness and an inspiration to those better things he is capable of achieving. Much of what we know and see of ancient Egyptian art is owed to the enterprise and vision of numerous generations of archaeologists and scholars from all over the world, whose common efforts have contributed to the knowledge of a civilization that marks the dawn of the human spirit. Prominent among the earliest and most active sponsors of archaeological work in Egypt are the Boston and Metropolitan Museums, whose centenary also marks a hundred years of excavations in my country. In sharing the responsibilities of this work between foreign and Egyptian bodies, we underline the international character of Egypt's art. The U.A.R., being fully aware of this particular vocation, regards the wealth of Egyptian Antiquities as a sacred trust which rests in our hands for the greater glory of mankind.

By the same token, a renewed international participation is needed to preserve one of the most beautiful and famous monuments of ancient Egypt, the Temple of Philae. UNESCO has undertaken a world-wide campaign toward this end; and the Boston and Metropolitan Museums

IV Relief from the tomb of Djehuty-hotpe

have graciously offered to turn over any profits realized from the present exhibition to UNESCO for the preservation of Philae.

As we in the United Arab Republic salute the beginning of the second century of the two Museums, we hope in turn that those who view this exhibition will remember that Philae belongs not to the U.A.R. alone, but to the entire world.

May the second one hundred years of the Museum of Fine Arts and The Metropolitan Museum of Art find a success redoubled beyond that of the first.

HONORARY COMMITTEE

Chairman, Dr Gamal Mokhtar, Under-Secretary of State for Antiquities, Ministry of Culture

Dr Magdi Wahba, Under-Secretary of State for Cultural Relations, Ministry of Culture

Mr John Richardson, Assistant Secretary for Cultural Affairs, Department of State

Mr Dillon Ripley, Secretary, The Smithsonian Institution

EXECUTIVE COMMITTEE

Chairman, Dr Gamal Mehrez, Director-General, Department of Antiquities

Dr Henri Riad, Director, Egyptian Museum, Cairo

Dr Sobhy el Bakri, Sub-Director for Pharaonic Antiquities, Department of Antiquities

Dr Zaki Iskander, Director, Department of Technical Affairs, Department of Antiquities

Dr Gamal Salem, First Keeper, Egyptian Museum, Cairo

Dr Abdel Qader Selim, First Keeper, Egyptian Museum, Cairo

Mr Perry T. Rathbone, Director, Museum of Fine Arts, Boston

Mr Thomas P. F. Hoving, Director, The Metropolitan Museum of Art, New York

Mr Kenneth Donahue, Director, Los Angeles County Museum of Art

PREFACE

On the occasion of the 100th Anniversary of both The Metropolitan Museum of Art and the Museum of Fine Arts, Boston, it is with great pride that the two institutions present what is unquestionably the finest exhibition of Egyptian antiquities ever seen in the United States.

It is particularly appropriate that The Metropolitan Museum and the Museum of Fine Arts should exhibit these extraordinary masterpieces from the Egyptian Museum, Cairo, during their Centennial celebrations. Egyptian art and archaeology were among the first concerns of the two museums as they built their collections. Since the beginning of the century both museums have excavated extensively in Egypt (always with the co-operation of the Egyptian Department of Antiquities). As a result of these excavations the collections of the two American museums and that of the Egyptian Museum have been handsomely enriched. Indeed, some of the objects in this great exhibition were discovered during these museum digs.

The Egyptian departments of both The Metropolitan Museum and the Museum of Fine Arts have been closely associated since their founding. While Boston's department of Egyptian art was established four years before New York's, both departments began under the direction of Albert M. Lythgoe. Lythgoe took up the curatorship in New York in 1906, at which time he was succeeded by George A. Reisner in Boston. Under the guidance of such outstanding Egyptologists as Lythgoe, H. E. Winlock, and William C. Hayes in New York, and Reisner, Dows Dunham, and William Stevenson Smith in Boston, the two museums have assembled the greatest collections of ancient Egyptian art in America.

The exhibition opens first at the Museum of Fine Arts, which took the initiative in organizing it and made its curatorial and technical resources available throughout this complex undertaking. For the cogent reason that relatively little Egyptian art has been exhibited west of the Great Divide, the loan has been extended, following its presentation in New York, to include the Los Angeles County Museum of Art. This extension to Los Angeles was brought about through the efforts of Kenneth Donahue, Director of the Los Angeles County Museum of Art, and Rexford Stead, Deputy Director.

The decision to send this unparalleled loan to the Western Hemisphere was influenced considerably by the desire on the part of all concerned to draw attention to the remarkable work being done through UNESCO to salvage and restore the great Nubian monuments, and in particular to attract support for the projected restoration of the superb Ptolomaic Temple at Philae.

On behalf of our respective Trustees, we wish to express our appreciation to the United Arab Republic, which has generously consented to lend these splendid national treasures. We want to thank in particular the Egyptian Minister of Culture, Dr Sarwat Okasha; Mr Abd-el Moneim El-Sawy; Dr Magdi Wahba and Dr Gamal Mokhtar. We are also indebted for their encouragement and advice to Dr Henri Riad, Director of the Egyptian Museum, Cairo, and Dr Zaki Iskander, Director of the Department of Technical Affairs, Department of Antiquities. Many hours were spent with them and with Dr Mokhtar; they patiently gave their assistance in determining the potential choices. Negotiations were greatly aided by the personal efforts of Dr Edmundo Lassalle, Counsellor on Egyptian Affairs to the Boston Museum, and Mrs Lassalle, who visited Cairo for this purpose on two occasions. At all times we were able to rely on the help of U.S. Foreign Service officers, Mr Donald Bergus, Mr Gordon Brown and Mr Eugene Bovis; and on Mr John Dorman, Mr Z. Misketian and Madame Atteya Habachi of the staff of the American Research Center in Egypt. Two of Egypt's foremost scholars, Dr Labib Habachi and Dr Ahmed Fakhry, were of great assistance. Mr Duncan Smith, Exhibits Designer of the Museum of Fine Arts, travelled to Egypt to study the problems of dismantling monumental sculptures and their reinstallation. Mr William J. Young, Head of the Research Laboratory at Boston, was on the spot to supervise the conservation, packing and transport of the forty-three objects. As many of them present special problems, Mr Young is overseeing the movement and handling of the exhibition throughout its stay in the United States.

Dr Edward L. B. Terrace, Associate Curator of the Department of Egyptian Art of the Museum of Fine Arts, has devoted much of his efforts during nearly two years in Egypt to every phase of the negotiations and the subsequent tasks. Dr Henry G. Fischer, Curator of Egyptian Art at The Metropolitan Museum shared with Dr Terrace the responsibility of making the final selection of objects for the exhibition. Together they have prepared this publication. Miss Lisa Cook, at The Metropolitan Museum Centennial Office, assisted in co-ordinating the arrangements among the three museums.

To all our friends and colleagues, Egyptian and American, we offer profound thanks for their indispensable services in producing a great international exhibition.

THOMAS P. F. HOVING

PERRY T. RATHBONE

INTRODUCTION

The present exhibition brings together many of the renowned masterpieces of the Egyptian Museum in Cairo. The aim of the selection has been to illustrate the leading pieces from Cairo, and it therefore follows that such a selection provides us with several of the principal masterpieces of ancient Egyptian art known. Another aim of the selection has been to supplement the collections in Boston and New York. Thus, the Third Dynasty reliefs of Hesy-Ra and Khai-bau-Sokar (nos. 4, 5), themselves masterpieces of sculpture in relief, provide an introduction to the Boston Museum's famous collection of Fourth Dynasty sculpture. By the same token, the splendid diorite statue of Chephren (no. 6), probably the greatest piece of Egyptian sculpture preserved, now joins for the first time its fellows in Boston, and augments the collection in New York, which is not so rich in sculpture of the Old Kingdom. On the other hand, the Middle Kingdom sculptures (nos. 14–18) fill out a period which is relatively weak in Boston and much stronger in New York. However, it is possible now to compare in the same building the finest statue of a private woman from the Middle Kingdom, the statue of the Lady Sennuy in Boston, with the best preserved overlife-size statue of a Queen of the Middle Kingdom, that of Nofret (no. 14). The two groups of jewellery, illustrating the impact of foreign influence in the Twelfth Dynasty (no. 13) and the period immediately preceding the New Kingdom (no. 19), add to the wealth of royal jewellery to be seen in New York and provide the Boston audience with its first opportunity to view such material.

The emphasis of the exhibition is on sculpture, especially sculpture in the round, because this is the art *par excellence* of ancient Egypt. It allowed the sculptor full scope for his skills and interests, whether they were to create such classically ideal images of kingship as those of Chephren (no. 6) and Tuthmosis III (no. 22), or to produce representations of actuality such as the dwarf Seneb (no. 12) or the great portraits of Amenemhat III (no. 17) and those of the Late Period (Mentuemhat, no. 37; Psamtik-sa-Neith, no. 39). No other culture has had so strong a tradition of representing man in stone sculpture. At the beginning of her history, Egypt achieved the highest standard in the art of sculpture, and without wavering, held to this standard for more than 3,000 years.

Formality was often relieved by informality and sobriety by humour in the decorations of temples and tomb chapels, as in the case of the billing birds (no. 8) and the fallen boatman (no. 11) of two Old Kingdom reliefs and the extraordinarily lively dancers of a relief of the Nineteenth Dynasty (no. 33). More specifically humorous, but with an underlying bite of satire, is the papyrus of cats and mice acting out the roles of men (no. 34); and if the representation of the obese Queen of Punt is based on the observation of a curious reality, it also reveals the strain of humour almost always present in the Egyptian artist.

While the exhibition does not serve as a summary of Egyptian art, it covers the entire span of ancient Egyptian history beginning with one of the first monuments of pharaonic Egypt, the Libya Palette (no. 1), and concluding with one of the last of the Roman Emperors who lived on the threshhold of the Middle Ages (no. 43). The exhibition includes painting and jewellery as well as sculpture, and therefore represents the principal arts of ancient Egypt. Finally, while the exhibition offers various aspects of Egyptian art that are important for the knowledge they give the historian of ancient Egyptian art, it must be said quite frankly that the chief basis of selection has been the superb quality represented by these forty-three works of art.

SPELLING OF NAMES: We follow the consistent practice of Egyptologists, which is to employ an inconsistent system.

CHRONOLOGY: For the most part, the dates given here are those employed by the authors of the revised edition of the *Cambridge Ancient History* with the following exceptions: (1) The approximate date of the beginning of the First Dynasty is here thought to be about 3000 BC; (2) For the Late Period, after the Twenty-first Dynasty, the chronology used by B. V. Bothmer, *ESLP*, is followed.

MATERIALS: The identification of materials given here is based on visual examination only. The attentive reader will note that certain objects identified here as greywacke are often published as being made of basalt or schist. When this inconsistency occurs, it is almost certain that the object in question is not basalt, but only a petrographic examination would demonstrate the certainty of its being schist or greywacke. Greywacke is used here because it was the more frequently employed material, although schist too is known from ancient Egypt.

SYSTEM OF NUMBERING OBJECTS IN THE CAIRO MUSEUM: *Cat. gén.* indicates that the object is published in one of the volumes of the *Catalogue général du Musée du Caire*, of which Dr George Reisner, Director of the Boston Museum's Expedition in Egypt, was one of the founding authors and a member of the original Catalogue Commission. The objects of the exhibition published in the *Catalogue général* are to be found in Borchardt, *Statuen*, Borchardt, *Denkmäler*, and Legrain, *Statues*. In the Bibliographies of the objects so published, it has been thought unnecessary to add more specific references to these volumes. *J. d'E.* indicates the *Journal d'Entrée* of the Cairo Museum, in which the objects are registered as they enter the museum. Still a third rubric is employed, that of the temporary register of the museum. In this catalogue the numbers are written as follows: 14–7/35–6 (= no. 35 here). In the register they occur as $\begin{array}{c|c}14&7\\ \hline 35&6\end{array}$, indicating that the object was the sixth to be registered on the 14th of July 1935. Numbers written on the objects themselves are usually red or black, those in red are invariably *Cat. gén.* numbers, those in black *J. d'E.*

BIBLIOGRAPHIES: Nearly every object exhibited has been published innumerable times. Therefore the Bibliography of each item is, for the most part, restricted to the essential publications only.

One of the pleasures of preparing such a catalogue as this is to observe previously unnoticed details of the objects themselves and connections they may have with other pieces. An even greater pleasure is afforded by the opportunity of providing others with material for new discussion and insights. The authors of this catalogue particularly hope their comments will be used for this purpose.

EDWARD L. B. TERRACE
Museum of Fine Arts, Boston

Chronological Table

With references to items in the Catalogue

BEGINNING OF DYNASTIC PERIOD (*c.* 3000 BC)	1
ARCHAIC PERIOD: DYNASTIES I–II (*c.* 3000–2686 BC)	2
OLD KINGDOM	
Dynasty III (*c.* 2686–2613 BC)	
Djoser (*c.* 2658–2649 BC)	3, 4, 5
Dynasty IV (*c.* 2613–2494 BC)	
Chephren (*c.* 2558–2533 BC)	6
Mycerinus (*c.* 2528–2500 BC)	7
Dynasty V (*c.* 2494–2345 BC)	
Weserkaf (*c.* 2494–2487 BC)	8, 9, 10, 11
Dynasty VI (*c.* 2345–2181 BC)	12
MIDDLE KINGDOM: DYNASTY XII (1991–1786 BC)	
Amenemhet II (1929–1895 BC)	13
Sesostris II (1897–1843 BC)	14
Sesostris III (1878–1843 BC)	15, 16
Amenemhet III (1842–1797 BC)	17, 18
SECOND INTERMEDIATE PERIOD: DYNASTIES XIII–XVII (1786–1567 BC)	
Dynasty XVII	
Seqenenre II	
Kamose	

V Amenophis II

following pages

VI Statue of Tuthmosis III

VII The wife of Nakht-Min

VIII Papyrus of Here-ubekhet

ABBREVIATIONS

Acta Orientalia	*Acta Orientalia ediderunt Societates Orientales Batava Danica Norvegica*, Leiden and Copenhagen
AJA	*American Journal of Archaeology*, Princeton, New Jersey
AJSL	*American Journal of Semitic Languages and Literatures*, Chicago
Ancient Egypt	*Ancient Egypt*, London
Annual Bibliog.	*Annual Egyptological Bibliography* (ed. J. M. A. Janssen), Leiden
Apollo	*Apollo: the Magazine of the Arts*, London
ASAE	*Annales du Service des Antiquités de l'Égypte*, Cairo
AZ	*Zeitschrift für ägyptische Sprache und Alterthumskunde*, Leipzig
BIFAO	*Bulletin de l'Institut Français d'Archéologie Orientale*, Cairo
BMFA	*Bulletin of the Museum of Fine Arts*, Boston
Borchardt, *Denkmäler*	Ludwig Borchardt, *Denkmäler des Alten Reiches (ausser den Statuen)*, 2 vols. (*Cat. gén.*), Cairo, 1937, 1964
Borchardt, *Statuen*	Ludwig Borchardt, *Statuen und Statuetten von Königen und Privatleuten*, 5 vols. (*Cat. gén.*), Cairo, 1911–1936
Bothmer, *ESLP*	Bothmer, B. V., *Egyptian Sculpture of the Late Period*, Brooklyn, 1960, repr. 1969
Cat. gén.	*Catalogue général des antiquités égyptiennes du Musée du Caire*
Chron. d'Ég.	*Chronique d'Egypte*, Brussels
Festschrift Ebers	*Aegyptiaca: Festschrift für Georg Ebers*, Leipzig, 1897
5000 Years Catalogue	*5000 Years of Egyptian Art*, an exhibition from the U.A.R. circulated in Europe, 1960–62. In each exhibition objects were added from collections from outside the U.A.R. Therefore there is no uniformity in the numbering of the various catalogues. In the present catalogue the abbreviation *5000 Years*

Catalogue designates an object from the Egyptian Museum, Cairo, that appeared in the exhibitions of 1960–62. In some cases it has been necessary to refer specifically to the individual catalogues of the exhibition; otherwise a list is given here of the cities in which the exhibition was held:
Brusselles, Palais des Beaux-Arts (1960)
Amsterdam, Rijksmuseum (1960)
Zürich, Kunsthaus (1961)
Essen, Villa Hügel (1961)
Stockholm, National Museum (1961)
Vienna, Kunstlerhaus (1961–62)
Denmark, Louisiana (1962)
London, Royal Academy of Arts (1962)
In 1963 another, but rather different, exhibition from the Museums of the U.A.R. was sent to Japan. The catalogue is in Japanese.

Gardiner, *Grammar*	Alan H. Gardiner, *Egyptian Grammar*, 3rd ed., London, 1957
Gardiner, *Onomastica*	Alan H. Gardiner, *Ancient Egyptian Onomastica*, 3 vols. London, 1947
Hayes, *Scepter*	William C. Hayes, *The Scepter of Egypt: A Background for the Study of the Egyptian Antiquities in the Metropolitan Museum of Art*, 2 vols. New York, 1953, 1959
ILN	*Illustrated London News*, London
JARCE	*Journal of the American Research Center in Egypt*, Boston
JEA	*Journal of Egyptian Archaeology*, London
J. d'E.	*Journal d'Entrée* (Cairo Museum entry numbers)
Jéquier, *Décoration Égyptienne*	Gustave Jéquier, *Décoration Égyptienne*, Paris, 1911
Jéquier, *Frises d'objets*	Gustave Jéquier, *Les Frises d'objets des sarcophages du moyen empire* (*MIFAO* 47), Cairo, 1921
JNES	*Journal of Near Eastern Studies*, Chicago
Junker, *Gîza*	Hermann Junker, *Gîza (Akademia der Wissenschaften in Wien. Ph.-hist. Kl. Denkschriften)*, 12 vols. Vienna, 1929–55
Kodansha	Kodansha (publisher), *Museums of the World: The Egyptian Museum, Cairo* (Japanese text), Tokyo, 1968
Kush	*Kush, Journal of the Sudan Antiquities Service*, Khartoum
Lange and Hirmer, *Egypt*	K. Lange and M. Hirmer, *Egypt, Architecture, Sculpture, Painting*, 4th ed., London, 1968
Legrain, *Statues*	Georges Legrain, *Statues et Statuettes de rois et de particuliers*, 3 vols. (*Cat. gén.*), Cairo, 1906–14
Lucas	A. Lucas, *Ancient Egyptian Materials and Industries*, 4th ed., revised by J. R. Harris, London, 1962
MDIK	*Mitteilungen des Deutschen Archäologischen Instituts Abteilung Kairo*, Wiesbaden

MIFAO	*Mémoires publiés par les membres de l'Institut français d'Archéologie Orientale du Caire*, Cairo
PM	Bertha Porter and Rosalind Moss, *Topographic Bibliography of Ancient Egyptian Hieroglyphic Texts, Reliefs and Paintings*, 7 vols. Oxford, 1927–51. Second ed. of vol. 1, in two parts, 1960–64
PSBA	*Proceedings of the Society of Biblical Archaeology*, London
Rev. de l'Égypte	*Revue de l'Égypte Ancienne*, Paris
Rev. d'Ég.	*Revue d'Égyptologie*, Paris
Smith, *Ancient Egypt*, 1960	W. S. Smith, *Ancient Egypt as Represented in the Museum of Fine Arts, Boston*, Boston, 1960
Smith, *Art and Architecture*	W. S. Smith, *The Art and Architecture of Ancient Egypt* (Pelican History of Art), Harmondsworth, Middlesex, 1958
Smith, *HESPOK*	W. S. Smith, *A History of Egyptian Sculpture and Painting in the Old Kingdom*, 2nd ed., London, 1949
Tel	A. Vigneau (photographer), *Le Musée du Caire (Encyclopedie photographique de l'art*, editions 'Tel'), Paris, 1949
Toutankhamon et son temps	Exhibition catalogue: *Toutankhamon et son temps, Petit Palais*, Feb. 17, 1967
Vandier, *Manuel*	Jacques Vandier, *Manuel d'archéologie égyptienne*, 5 vols. Paris 1952–69
Vernier, *Bijoux*	Émile Vernier, *Bijoux et orfèvreries*, 3 vols. (*Cat. gén.*) Cairo, 1925–27

PHOTOGRAPHIC ACKNOWLEDGEMENTS: The black and white plates are by Costa, Cairo, with the exception of those on pages 26, 42 and 106 which are by John G. Ross, and pages 22, 58, 114 (below) and 118 (below) which are by courtesy of the Egyptian Museum, Cairo. The jacket photograph and colour plates I, V and VI are by John G. Ross, plates II and VIII by Mohammed Fathi Desouq, III and VII by Peter A. Clayton, and IV by Albert Shoucair.

1 The Libya Palette

Catalogue général 14238

One of the most common artifacts of the Predynastic Period is the schist palette, on which malachite was ground to provide a green eye paint that was both cosmetic and hygienic. Traces of this paint may be seen on painted sculpture of the Archaic Period down through the Third Dynasty, as exemplified by the niche of Khai-bau-Sokar (no. 5).

With the advent of the First Dynasty, the cosmetic palette, often enlarged to monumental proportions, became the vehicle of a series of reliefs depicting hunts or military victories. Apart from the famous Narmer Palette, the fragment shown here is the most imposing example of this series in the Cairo Museum.

The existing lower part of the monument shows no trace of the circular rimmed area that was reserved for the eye paint, so that it is not possible to distinguish between recto and verso. On both sides the representations face right and are to be read towards the left in accordance with the orientation of Egyptian writing, a recent innovation inspired by contact with Sumer. It is also apparent that the artist laid them out in the same order, for nearly every register shows a certain degree of crowding at the left end. The style of the relief is more archaic and lively than that of the Narmer Palette, on which, for example, a bull similarly shows a series of wrinkles over the eyes, prominent veins on the muzzle and legs, and a series of grooves on the shoulder, but shows them much less emphatically (page 22).

The bulls of the Libyan Palette appear in the uppermost register of the side representing trees and livestock. There are four of them, and the last two not only diminish in length but increasingly overlap their predecessors. The register beneath shows an equal number of donkeys, each with the characteristic stripe on its shoulder; again there is a gradual decrease in the length of each animal. The same is true of the next register, which contains five rams, and in this case the last ram turns his head. In addition to utilizing the limited space to best advantage, the turned head also relieves the monotony of the composition, and this device is frequently employed in later Egyptian art. At the bottom is a grove of trees, formerly identified as olive trees, in front of which is a combination of hieroglyphs—a throwstick (𓌙) atop the sign meaning 'land' (𓈅). This monogram represents Tjehenu, a region which was situated at the western edge of the Nile Delta and may have included part of the Libyan coast. According to the Palermo Stone, a total of 13,100 cattle were brought away from Tjehenu at the beginning of the Fourth Dynasty, in the reign of

Sneferu, and, at the beginning of the Fifth Dynasty, the temple of Sahure recorded a total of slightly more than 822,941 kine, donkeys, goats and sheep from the same quarter. Probably the palette similarly records booty, but it remains uncertain whether the trees are to be interpreted in the same way, as wood or oil brought back from Tjehenu, or whether they merely represent the wooded locale of the country in question.

The opposite side displays a series of seven cities, the buttressed walls of which are presented in plan. Within each enclosure a scattering of rectangular buildings is grouped around one or more hieroglyphs that identify the city. The detail from the Narmer palette (page 22) shows the same combination of elements, but the wall has been broken open by a bull, probably symbolizing the might of the king. In the present example the walls are intact, but they are besieged by a series of emblematic creatures, again representing aspects of royal power, which wield pointed mattocks. The names of the cities are represented by an owl, a crested bird (heron ?), a pair of wrestlers, a beetle (𓆣), a pair of arms and hands with thumbs joined (*ka*), a round-topped reed hut and a bush; the first is attacked by a falcon, the next by a Seth-animal(?), the fifth by a lion, and the others by a scorpion and a pair of falcons on standards. None of these can be linked with any certainty to places that are known from later sources, and one is free to surmise that they may be located in the land of Tjehenu.

The scene in the upper register represented human figures, for three feet are visible at the right edge. At least one of the figures to which they belong is in motion, and his activity is almost certainly related to a battle—a battle that is emblematically restated in the hieroglyphic groups below it. We are spared such grisly details as the row of decapitated warriors on the Narmer Palette, and are only affected by the naïve appeal of the animals: the wide-eyed simplicity of the herds, the bizarre activity of the animal sappers, and the comically lopsided expression on the face of the owl.

Said (by Emil Brugsch) to come from Abydos, beginning of First Dynasty, schist (greywacke), maximum breadth 21 cm., height 19 cm.

Bibliography: *PM* I, 105 (6). Later references: Elise Baumgartel, *The Cultures of Predynastic Egypt* II, pp. 102–4; Ludwig Keimer, *BIFAO* 31 (1931), pp. 121 ff.; *Annals of Faculty of Art, Ibrahim Pasha University* 1 (1951), 81; P. Newberry, *JEA* 37 (1951), 73 ff.; W. F. M. Petrie, *Ceremonial Slate Palettes*, pp. 14–15 and Pl. G (19–20); Siegfried Schott, *Hieroglyphen*, pp. 19–21 and Pl. 3, *Paideuma, Mitteilungen zur Kulturkunde* 4 (1950), 226–7; *Mitteilungen der Deutschen Orient-Gesellschaft zu Berlin*, No. 84 (Dec. 1952), 15–18; Vandier, *Manuel* I, Pt. 1, pp. 590–92; Kodansha, Pl. 49.

Comments: The name of Tjehenu was independently recognized in 1915 by Newberry and Sethe, who pointed out that the fusion of hieroglyphs is particularly common in the oldest inscriptions. For the location of the region see Gardiner, *Onomastica* I, pp. 116–19. The identification of the Seth-animal is suggested by Schott (*Hieroglyphen*), who errs, however, in viewing the round-topped hut as a reed mat (□ = Buto). Steindorff, in *Festschrift Ebers*, 123, points out that the beetle is four-legged and might be a frog; the phonetic complement beneath it (𓂋) seems to confirm the first alternative, however: *ḫprr*. I agree with Baumgartel that the scorpion is probably not to be regarded as a 'King Scorpion'.

H.G.F.

2 Kneeling Statue of a Priest

Catalogue général 1

The compactness of this statue, typical of all archaic sculpture in the round, is emphasized by its attitude, which is unusual. Instead of being seated upon a four-legged stool, as are most other statues of the first three dynasties, the figure kneels, with both legs under him and both hands flat upon his knees. There is no space between the limbs, nor any trace of that expedient commonly known as 'negative space' that is developed shortly before the Fourth Dynasty. The massive head is thrust forward; enveloped in a wig of overlapping locks, it dominates the body. Disproportionately large heads tend to occur in archaic periods as disparate as Sumerian, Romanesque and Benin, but this tendency continued much longer in Mesopotamia than it did in Egypt. Another feature which the archaic Egyptian statues have in common with their Mesopotamian counterparts is the location of all or part of the accompanying inscriptions on the body or garment of the person who is represented. In the succeeding period of the Old Kingdom the sculptor virtually always confined the inscription to the base, seat or back pillar of the statue, unless there was some appropriate alternative such as an inscribed belt or a papyrus unrolled across the lap. This reticence was never felt in Mesopotamia; in Egypt it was only very gradually relaxed, and very selectively. In the present case the principal inscription appears in relief across the upper front surface of the base. But a subordinate inscription is incised behind the right shoulder. It names, in correct sequence, the first three kings of the Second Dynasty, and evidently indicates that the individual was a priest of their funerary cults at Saqqara, and that he kneels before them. Saqqara was the earliest cemetery of Memphis, where the statue was excavated in 1888.

The incised inscription also indicates that the statue is no earlier than the mid-Second Dynasty and may, of course, be somewhat later. The form of the wig and the treatment of the face seem to bring it somewhat closer to the Old Kingdom, as does the fact that the main inscription is on the base. This inscription identifies the owner, but it is difficult to explain in its entirety. The column of signs at the beginning remains uncertain; but the rest seems to consist of a title 'Great of incense in the Red House' and the name Hotep-dif.

From Mit Rahina (site of Memphis), late Second Dynasty or, more probably, Third Dynasty, red granite, height 39 cm.

BIBLIOGRAPHY: *PM* III, 226; Borchardt, *Statuen* I, pp. 1–2 and pl. 1; G. Maspero, *Le Musée Egyptien* I, pp. 12–13 and pl. 13; A. Shoukry, *Die Privatgrabstatuen im alten Reich*, pp. 20–24 and fig. 1; Smith, *HESPOK*, p. 15 and pl. 2; Vandier, *Manuel* I, 979–81 and fig. 655; W. Wolf, *Die Kunst Agyptens*, pp. 60–61 and fig. 33; H. G. Fischer, *Artibus Asiae* 24 (1961), 45–6.

COMMENTS: For the attitude *cf.* Cairo *Cat. gén.* 119, a Fifth Dynasty kneeling statue that is clearly identified as a funerary priest and was placed in the tomb of the man whose cult the priest served. Later the same attitude is known in royal statuary, when the king offers two pots of myrrh; the earliest example known is Brooklyn 39.121 (Pepy I).

H.G.F.

3 Schist Dish Imitating Basketry

Journal d'Entrée 71298

The panelled wall around the precincts of King Djoser's Step Pyramid encloses what might be called a petrified palace. Transformed into limestone, doors are frozen ajar, wattle fences are congealed into massive relief, bundled reeds coalesce into stately columns. It is therefore appropriate that, among the many thousands of stone vessels placed in the corridors beneath the eastern side of the pyramid, Lauer and Quibell found several baskets made of schist. While many of Djoser's utensils for the hereafter are inscribed with the names of earlier rulers, the excavators felt that these imitations of basket work must belong to the Third Dynasty. One of them is almost identical to the example shown here, but is somewhat inferior in workmanship. During the First Dynasty schist dishes were carved with a virtuosity that seemed altogether to disregard the brittleness of the material. This example, from a Second Dynasty tomb, shows almost equal craftsmanship and ingenuity, but is far more durable. At one corner, on the upper edge, is the word 'gold' (𓋞). An open tray is hardly a very safe repository for anything so valuable, and one can only surmise that it may have been used for the formal presentations of gold necklaces to the king or to his courtiers.

From Emery's excavations at North Saqqara, 1937–8, schist (greywacke), length 22.7 cm., width 14 cm.

Bibliography: W. B. Emery, *Archaic Egypt*, pl. 39 (6); *5000 Years Catalogue*, Essen, no. 8; *5000 Years Catalogue*, London, no. 13.

Comments: For the comparable dish from the Step Pyramid, gallery VI, see J.-Ph. Lauer and J. E. Quibell, *ASAE* 35 (1935), 73, 79 and pls. 1 (18), 2 (4). The imitation of rushwork may also be compared to the faience and limestone matting on the walls of the principal underground chambers of the pyramid.

H.G.F.

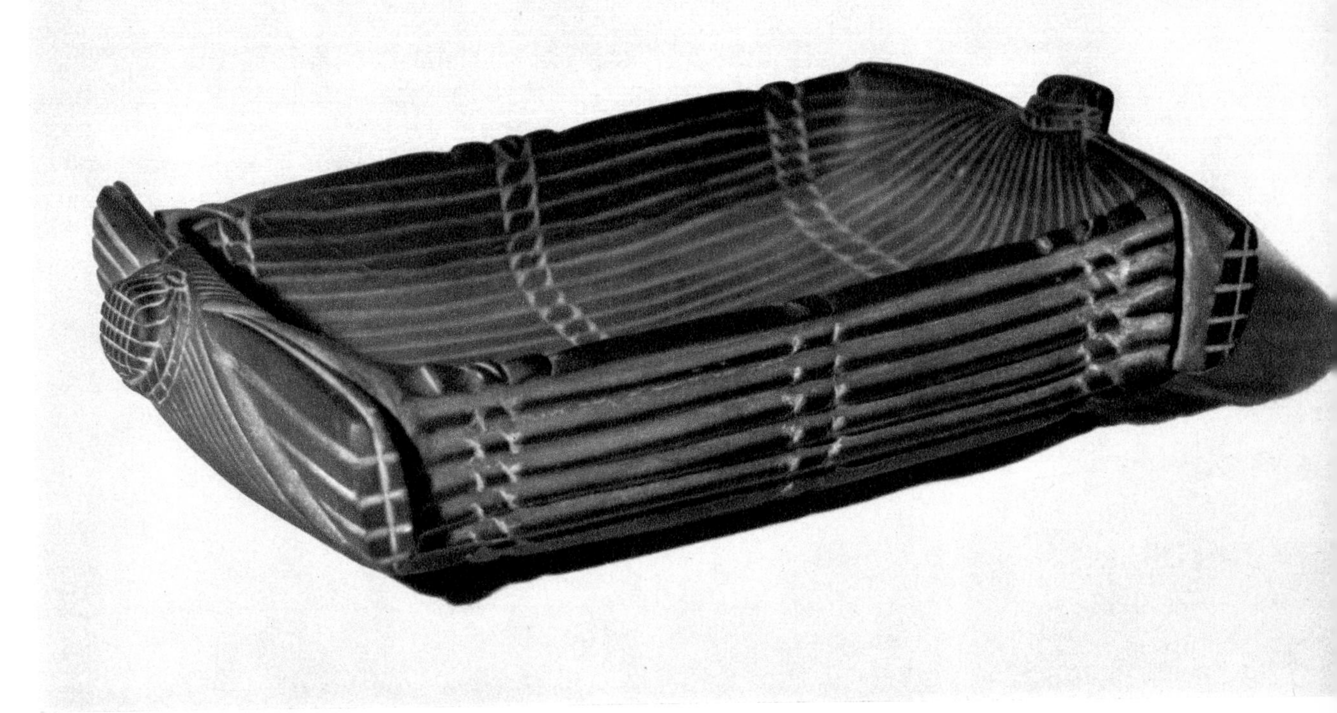

4 Wooden Panel of Hesy-Ra

Catalogue général 1427

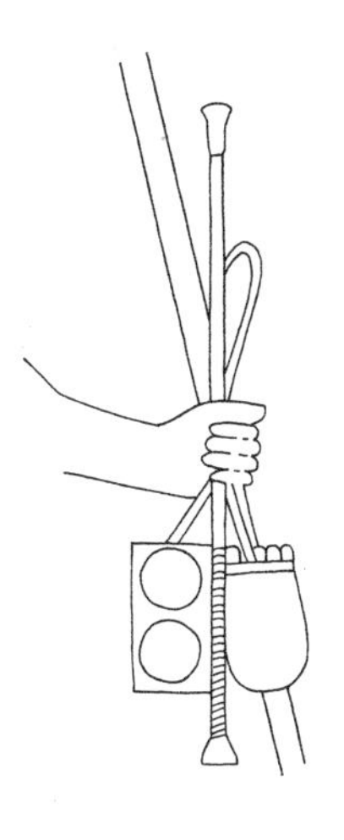

From a clay jar-sealing found in his burial chamber, we know that Hesy-Ra was an official of King Djoser, whose Step Pyramid enclosure was situated in the same necropolis, about a thousand yards southward. Of the five wooden panels that were recovered from the multiple-niched west wall of his narrow offering chamber, the one shown here is the best preserved. Here, as in all the other representations, he is shown holding the scribal kit—a palette with disks representing red and black ink, a long pen case, and a leather bag that perhaps contains a further supply of black pigment; in later representations this is replaced by a water jar (see figure). The same equipment appears in the last sign of his principal title, 'head of royal scribes' ([hieroglyphs]), which precedes his name. The inscription is arranged in four columns and, since the signs face toward the right, is read from that direction. The same orientation, which predominates in Egyptian monuments of all periods, is also applied to the large figure of Hesy-Ra, for this is itself a hieroglyphic 'determinative', an ideograph complementing the phonetic writing of the name.

The area at the top of the panel was probably traversed by a rounded lintel like that which surmounts the slightly later offering niche of Khai-bau-Sokar (no. 5). Below this, the slender and delicately carved hieroglyphs emerge from a slightly recessed rectangular ground. This ground is continued at the same width, but twice as much depth, to accommodate the equally slender representation of Hesy-Ra, so that the height of the relief increases in relation to the larger scale. Much of the elegance of the total effect is due to this sensitive relationship of levels, which occurs in two of the other four panels, and the effect is enhanced by the amount of space that is left around the figure and inscription. The spacing also brings together the figure and inscription, and so emphasizes their interdependence. Both have been executed with equal care, as may be seen from the details of the hieroglyph representing the word 'eldest': a gaunt but paunchy individual who wears a long kilt and leans on his staff.

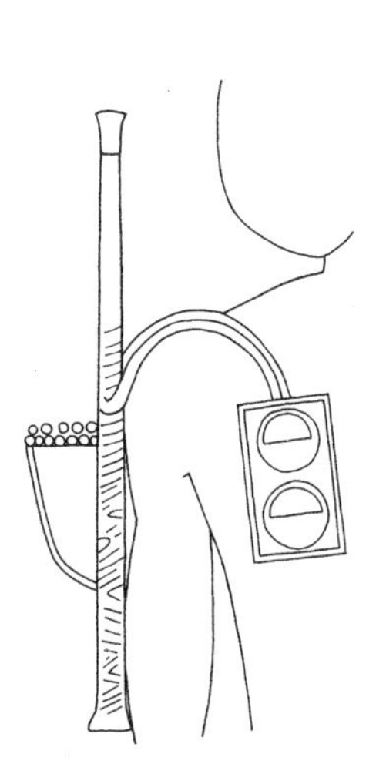

The figure of Hesy-Ra has the shoulder-length wig, short kilt, long staff and flat-ended baton of authority that are seen in countless later representations of Old Kingdom officials. The kilt is a simpler version of the one worn by Khai-bau-Sokar as described below (no. 5). His profile also shows some resemblance to that of Khai-bau-Sokar; both have a slightly aquiline nose, strongly defined mouth, and a moustache. The slanted ridge above his eyebrow suggests a look of frowning concentration such as appears in the early Fourth Dynasty statue of Ra-hotpe in the Cairo Museum. While the brow, upper lid of the eye and moustache are in stylized relief, and the lips are equally sharply defined, the structure of the face is otherwise handled with extraordinary subtlety, including such details as the philtrum, the nasolabial fold, a shorter fold at the corner of the mouth, and a slight fullness towards the rear of the jaw. His body is lean, the clavicles emerging plainly and, below them, a series of faint striations over the sternum; the pectoral (only one of them, as is usual in two-dimensional representations) is very gently rounded, its profile somewhat distorted by a crack that isolates the nipple; the muscles of the shoulders are similarly defined and there is a realistic distinction between the knotted muscles on the upper part of the straightened arm and the bunched muscles of the one that is flexed.

In common with most relief representations of men, the legs are somewhat unnaturally grooved, but the knees are rendered most convincingly. Both feet are presented as though viewed from the inside, for it was not until the later part of the Eighteenth Dynasty that this convention was abandoned. There is—as so frequently in Egyptian art at its best—a nice balance between the relatively flat areas and areas of patterned detail, such as the twisted strands of the wig, the upper part of which is emphasized by four horizontal waves, and the composite pleating of the pulled-up end of the kilt. All in all, the refinement of the relief is such that it is scarcely equalled in any succeeding period of Egyptian history.

From the northern edge of the Saqqara Cemetery, mid-Third Dynasty, wood, height 115 cm.

BIBLIOGRAPHY: *PM* III, 99: A. Mariette, *Les mastabas de l'ancien empire*, 81; J. Quibell, *Tomb of Hesy*, pp. 4–5 and pl. 29; Borchardt, *Denkmäler*, p. 109 and pl. 25; E. Drioton, *ASAE* 41 (1942), 93–5 and

fig. 13; Smith, *HESPOK*, 139–40 and *Art and Architecture*, p. 36; Lange and Hirmer, *Egypt*, pl. 18; *Tel*, Pl. 6; W. Wolf, *Die Kunst Aegyptens*, p. 200 and fig. 166; C. Aldred, *Old Kingdom Art in Egypt*, pl. 9; K. Michalowski, *The Art of Ancient Egypt*, pl. 67; J. Yoyotte, *Treasures of the Pharaohs*, p. 15; Kodansha, pl. 2 (colour).

COMMENTS: The accompanying figures are taken from Drioton's discussion of the scribe's kit. For the hieroglyph showing a long-kilted old man *cf. JNES* 18 (1959), 247, and *JARCE* 2 (1963), 23–24. The subtlety of the reliefs is demonstrated by Michalowski's colour plate, where the photographer's lighting has eliminated most of the modelling.

H.G.F.

5 Offering Niche of Khai-bau-Sokar

Catalogue général 1385

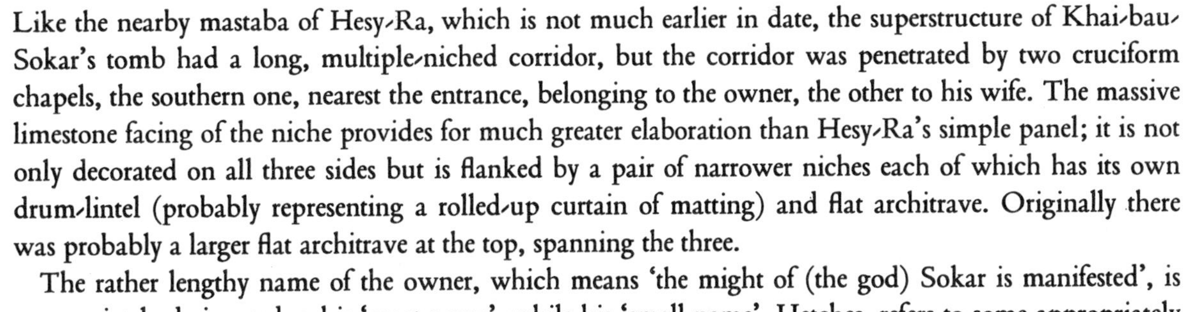

Like the nearby mastaba of Hesy-Ra, which is not much earlier in date, the superstructure of Khai-bau-Sokar's tomb had a long, multiple-niched corridor, but the corridor was penetrated by two cruciform chapels, the southern one, nearest the entrance, belonging to the owner, the other to his wife. The massive limestone facing of the niche provides for much greater elaboration than Hesy-Ra's simple panel; it is not only decorated on all three sides but is flanked by a pair of narrower niches each of which has its own drum-lintel (probably representing a rolled-up curtain of matting) and flat architrave. Originally there was probably a larger flat architrave at the top, spanning the three.

The rather lengthy name of the owner, which means 'the might of (the god) Sokar is manifested', is appropriately designated as his 'great name', while his 'small name', Hetches, refers to some appropriately diminutive species of mammal. His titles include several priestly functions, relating to the cults of Anubis, the jackal god who presided over the desert necropolis, Igai, the god of the western oases, the Upper Egyptian god Seth, and Seshat, goddess of writing and architecture. His other activities ranged from directing dancers to the management of breweresses, but he was most particularly concerned with carpenters and other craftsmen. As 'director of craftsmen' he was entitled to wear the collar of the high priest of Memphis, which curiously incorporates an elongated jackal who bends a pair of human hands in adoration (see figure).

At the rear of the niche Khai-bau-Sokar sits on a stool, the legs of which imitate those of a bull. One arm and shoulder emerges from a long cloak, the hand outstretched towards a table laden with half-loaves of bread. The inscription above the table enumerates benefactions that he is to receive, and for this reason the hieroglyphs are reversed so that they address him; they provide a libation of water, the washing of hands, incense and perfumed ointment—all in preparation for the meal itself, which consists of wine, bread, fruit and various portions of flesh and fowl. 'A thousand of bread, beer, jars of ointment and clothing' is invoked beneath the table. The bottom half of the wall is filled with a more organized and inclusive tabulation of offerings. The upper compartments represent various kinds and qualities of cloth; below these are an assortment of vessels, a brazier, five kinds of oil, three kilts, and three pieces of furniture—a bed, chest, and headrest. 'A thousand' of each is specified. At the very bottom a separate section lists a steer, a crane, a goose, and then three heaps of grain and dried fruit. On the sides of the niche the list is continued with a register devoted to beverages, including beer and two kinds of wine, and a second register again listing fruits.

Although the limestone reliefs are bolder and less delicate than those of Hesy-Ra, the hieroglyphs are similarly proportioned and, particularly on the sides of the niche, the face of Khai-bau-Sokar is depicted with an equal measure of realistic detail. His nose is somewhat more aquiline, his mouth heavier, his moustache more drooping, but all these features nonetheless make for a certain resemblance. The eyebrow is not indicated in relief, but the forehead is more distinctly furrowed—perhaps by wrinkles rather than a frown—but the comparable examples of Hesy-Ra and Ra-hotpe favour the second possibility. In any case, the naso-labial fold is more pronounced, and there is the suggestion of a pouch beneath the eye. A difference in age is also indicated by a heavier torso and limbs, and swelling abdomen. It should be noted, however, that the left-hand figure appears to have absorbed more offerings than the one on the right. Both of these standing figures wear the elaborate necklace of the Memphite high priest, as remarked earlier; their rather tight-fitting wig shows three tiers of short overlapping locks, and their kilt is partially cross-pleated, so that one end can be drawn up and tucked under the belt. Possibly the plain edge schematically indicates that the pleating has pulled to the point that the pattern disappears. The projecting tab is also cross-pleated, as in the case of Hesy-Ra, and is held in place by a bow knot.

Since the figures on the side panels both face outward, the left one is a mirror image of the usual orientation, which shows the baton of office in the right hand, the staff in the left. It will be noticed, however, that in this reversal the hands are presented as though they were seen from the back, and that the baton accordingly passes behind the kilt (see figure). This fusion of front and rear is a clear and striking example of the Egyptian draftsman's willingness to combine disparate points of view.

The entire niche was originally painted, and some remnants of colour may still be seen. The narrow supplementary niches were yellow, the hair of the figures was black, the skin red, and the kilt white with yellow cross-pleating. There are traces of green beneath the eyes.

From the northern edge of the Saqqara Cemetery, late-Third Dynasty, painted limestone, height 195 cm.

BIBLIOGRAPHY: *PM* III, 100; A. Mariette, *Les mastabas de l'ancien empire*, pp. 71, 74–9; M. A. Murray, *Saqqara Mastabas* I, p. 3 and pls. 1–2, II, pp. 1–12 and pl. 1; Borchardt, *Denkmäler* I, pp. 44–7, and pl. 10; Smith, *HESPOK*, pp. 149, 150 and pl. 36 (a), and *Art and Architecture*, p. 37 and fig. 10; H. Fischer, *JNES* 18 (1959), 244–5 and fig. 9, and *AZ* 93 (1966), 64; E. Staehelin, *Untersuchungen zur ägyptischen Tracht im Alten Reich*, pp. 14–15, 135–9, 185 and fig. 14; W. Barta, *Die altägyptische Opferliste*, pp. 32–5 and fig. 2.

COMMENTS: For a further example of the Memphite high priest's necklace in the Old Kingdom see Staehelin, p. 136, who believes that the necklace of no. 10 originally had this form; also Borchardt, *ibid.*, vol. II, pp. 177–8 and pl. 100 (*Cat. gén.* 1756); contrary to Borchardt's sketch, the jackal again raises a pair of arms. The kilt of this high priest shows a row of five tassels at the bottom, which probably represent the end of a painted 'sporran' and are not to be compared with the tabs at the bottom of Khai-bau-Sokar's kilt. W. S. Smith initially placed Khai-bau-Sokar at the end of the Third Dynasty, but ultimately felt he might be as early as the middle. According to Barta, the form of the offering list definitely confirms the first alternative; he assigns the list to the end of the dynasty. For the form of the list, see also W. S. Smith, 'The Old Kingdom Linen List', *AZ* 71 (1935), 134–49, and Jéquier, *Frises d'objets*, 33–8.

H.G.F.

6 Chephren, The Living Horus

Catalogue général 14

This statue is undoubtedly the supreme sculpture from ancient Egypt and one of the great masterpieces of art. It is an unequalled image of the ideal man and of god incarnate in man created by a nameless master for Chephren, builder of the Second Pyramid and the king whose audacious sculptors carved the Sphinx from the living rock of the Giza plateau—the first colossal sculpture of man. The enthroned diorite Chephren makes a statement of dignity and beauty so simple, so straightforward as to produce an image of man in as ideal a form as he has ever aspired to.

The king is seated on a throne the legs of which are composed of the fore- and rear-parts of lions. On the sides of the throne are the insignia of the Two Lands, the plant of Upper Egypt and the papyrus of Lower Egypt knotted together around the symbol of unity, *sma*, the hieroglyphic sign of the lungs and windpipe. These elements are carved in high, bold relief against the block of the seat. Although the throne appears to have a high back, the slab is actually a reminiscence of the block from which the sculpture was carved (*cf.* nos. 7 and 10). Like most Old Kingdom seated statues, other sculptures of Chephren do not have this slab. Most of the works in which this feature appears come from the principal studios, royal or official. Here it not only emphasizes the elemental structure of the sculpture; it also serves as a support for the falcon whose outspread wings embrace the head of the king. This falcon is the god Horus, a primeval animistic deity of the sky, whose syncretism with the sun occurred very early, probably already in prehistoric times. Commonly, the falcon of Chephren is described as protecting the king. Certainly, however, the great bird signifies that Chephren is the Living Horus, the god manifest in the person of the king.

The king wears the royal *nemes* headcloth (only the lappets are grooved) and the *shendyt* kilt, which is pleated all over. The base of the uraeus begins above the relief band of the lower edge of the wig. The cobra's hood is decorated with a vertical band in relief. It should be noted that the transition of the upper folds of the *nemes* is as smoothly modelled as the muscles connecting chests with shoulders in both this sculpture and that of Mycerinus (no. 7). The king rests his left hand flatly on his knee, while his right clenched fist holds a folded cloth.

The construction of the throne has a logic not unlike that of the statue of Hathor and Psamtik (no. 38) made 2,000 years later. The rear legs (one on each side of the chair) are executed entirely in relief, and in

profile the front legs also appear to be almost in relief. However, from the front, we see that the lions' foreparts, including two legs on each side, are carved in the round, without, however, attributing to them any degree of realism. On the contrary, the lions are a kind of hieroglyph signifying 'throne'. The falcon is carved partly in the round, partly in relief, and stands proudly and powerfully on the top of the back slab, its legs carved in relief against the king's headcloth. The tail descends below the upper edge of the slab and is carved in relief against it. The head of the bird rises a few centimetres above the top of the crown.

The majestic dignity of this great sculpture is the result of the superb handling of the masses throughout. The falcon is as much an integral part of the sculptural volumes as any element of Chephren's body, the throne, or the back slab. Again, we must emphasize the elemental quality of the block—the quarried stone—from which the sculpture is carved. Allowing himself minute liberties like the head of the falcon which protrudes slightly above the crown, the artist has maintained the statue within the fundamental cuboid structure basic to all Egyptian sculpture. Perhaps never again did the aesthetic and iconographic aspects of ancient Egyptian art meet in such perfect harmony.

See also Colour Plate I.

From Giza, found in a pit in the granite Valley Temple of Chephren's Pyramid, 1858, Fourth Dynasty, height of figure to top of crown 136 cm., width at shoulders 52 cm., height of base 24 cm., width of back slab at feet of throne 57 cm., width of front of base 51.5 cm.

Bibliography: *PM* III, p. 6; Smith, *HESPOK*, pp. 33 ff., pl. 5, c; Vandier, *Manuel*, pl. II, 2–4; Lange and Hirmer, *Egypt*, pls. 30–31, IV (colour); Kodansha, pl. 6 (colour); and frequently elsewhere.

Comments: One other Fourth Dynasty king's head with a falcon in the same position is known (Boston 25–1–587), alabaster fragments of the wig preserved only. It was found near Cheop's Pyramid Temple, and Smith therefore considered it to belong to Cheop's reign, although he adds that fragments of Chephren were found in the same area (*HESPOK*, p. 20, pl. 5, a). The Brooklyn Museum has a small alabaster statuette of Pepi I of the Sixth Dynasty, in which a falcon with folded wings stands behind the king's head at right angles to it (C. Aldred, *Old Kingdom Art in Ancient Egypt*, pls. 62, 63). In this case, the falcon forms part of the titulary of the king written on the slab (The Horus Mery-tawy). Still later examples are known, *e.g. Cat. gén.* 743 (*cf. Manuel* III, p. 392 and pl. CXXV, 3) and *Cat. gén.* 42152 (*cf. Manuel* III, pl. CXXXII), both of the New Kingdom. On *Cat. gén.* 42152 the falcon rests at the back of the high *atef* crown that surmounts the round wig of Ramesses VI. In every case, except for the Brooklyn Pepi, the falcon is an element of the crown, the embodiment of kingship.

For the possible existence of two schools of sculpture at Giza in the Fourth Dynasty, see G. Reisner, *Mycerinus*, pp. 128–9, Smith, *HESPOK*, pp. 35–6, Terrace, *BMFA* 59(1961), 47 ff. In view of the fact that the triad no. 7 and the diorite Chephren are placed together in the school of 'Sculptor A', while showing considerable differences (the first more plastic, the latter more restrained), the merits of this hypothesis should perhaps be re-examined from the point of view of separating more precisely the different schools which certainly exist (*cf. Manuel* III, pp. 21 ff.).

E.L.B.T.

7 Triad of Mycerinus, the Goddess Hathor and Personification of the Dog Nome

Journal d'Entrée 40679

Much of our evidence for royal sculpture of the Fourth Dynasty comes from Reisner's excavations for the Museum of Fine Arts at the Valley and Pyramid Temples of Mycerinus, builder of the third and smallest of the Giza pyramids. From the Valley Temple came four complete group statues, each showing the king with the goddess Hathor and the personification of one of the nomes or provinces of Egypt. Three of these personifications are female; and there are one complete and one fragmentary male representation. With one exception, the king is shown, as here, standing between the two deities. The figures of king and deities are imbued with youthful vitality. Indeed, the modelling is remarkable and there is a rich display of naturalistic detail. It is unnecessary to point out here all the instances, but we may mention in particular the muscles of the arms, the muscles which join the breast and shoulders, the neck muscles, and the collar bones. Attention must also be paid to the treatment of abdomen and pelvis, as well as to the median line which rises upwards from the wide, depressed navel. With the exception of the upper lids which are in relief, the eyes and brows are particularly plastic.

The female figures wear skin-tight garments, the details of which were originally painted. Mycerinus wears the royal *shendyt* kilt, with protruding tab. His belt, in relief, is uninscribed and unadorned (*cf.* no. 10). The king carries the emblematic staves (*see* no. 10), and the deities hold the *shen* emblem at their sides. The nome figure has both feet planted firmly together, while Mycerinus and Hathor both step forward with the left foot.

Mycerinus wears the tall White Crown of Upper Egypt as he does in the three other complete triads. All four triads represent nomes of Upper Egypt. The deeply grooved wig of Hathor is adorned with her emblem, the cow's horns enclosing the sun. The personification of the nome, on the other hand, carries an elaborate nome-standard, of which the principal element is the so-called Anubis animal, with a feather on its back. The animal is a minor masterpiece of relief sculpture. Whereas the insignia of Hathor is an integral part of the sculpture, the nome standard is carved in relief on the background. It is to be noted that the two deities embrace the king, their hands emphasizing the balance already created in the symmetrical arrangement of the figures. It might be objected that these bodiless hands induce a jarring note in an otherwise masterfully conceived work.

On the triads Hathor is called 'Mistress of the Sycamore Shrine', a cult which apparently existed at Memphis. Thus she has here a double role—she represents the creative force of the sun and at the same time embodies the fertile aspects of vegetation. The nome figure is stated in the inscription to have brought 'all good things for the king forever'. And that, indeed, is the purpose of these triads, to provide the physical presence of food offerings from all the king's realms for his eternal life.

From Giza, Valley Temple of the Pyramid of Mycerinus, Fourth Dynasty, greywacke originally painted, height 93 cm., width front of base 39 cm., width back of base 47 cm., width top of back slab 44 cm. (corners slightly bevelled).

BIBLIOGRAPHY: *PM* III, p. 7; G. Reisner, *Mycerinus,* p. 109, pls. 38, c, 43, a–d, and chapter VII *passim;* Vandier, *Manuel*, III, pl. IV, 3; *5000 Years Catalogue*, London, no. 18, pl. VIII.

COMMENTS: The present, highly polished surface of the stone, so suitable to the rich modelling of the surfaces, was originally covered with paint, of which only a trace of a red collar can now be seen. The material of these statues and others is often mistakenly called slate or schist, and even basalt. In fact, it is a sedimentary stone called greywacke; see Lucas, pp. 419–20. Since this is the common material quarried from the Wadi Hammamat throughout Egyptian history, we shall use the term throughout this catalogue to describe sculpture made from what appears with the naked eye to be the same stone. The Boston triad (09.200) shows Hathor enthroned between the Hare Nome on the right and Mycerinus on the left. For a recent discussion of the two triads in Boston, see Terrace, *BMFA* 59(1961), 47 ff., although it is difficult to defend precisely the so-called 'Sculptors A and B' of Reisner; see Comment, no. 6. Although Reisner thought the deities might be holding seals, the emblems are probably the *shen*, which is the circular, original form of the cartouche, symbolizing the area encircled by the sun and later by the king in his role as a sun-god (Gardiner, *Grammar*, p. 74).

That the cylindrical objects clutched in the hands of stone sculptures are symbolic staves is surely proved by the Boston triad, where the throne of Hathor provides a resting place for a mace held by the king; see Bothmer, *BMFA* 48(1950)10 ff., especially pp. 15–16 (the Boston king holds what Bothmer believes to be the *nem-es* instrument in his left hand). It is curious that of the completely preserved triads, all represent Upper Egyptian nomes. In theory, there might have been personifications of all the nomes of Upper and Lower Egypt, perhaps as many as thirty-four, although the precise number of nomes in the Fourth Dynasty is unknown.

E.L.B.T.

8 Fragment of relief with two birds

6–9/32–1

One of the great glories of ancient Egyptian art was the development of the scenes from daily life which have given us an almost complete record of the amusements and works of the Egyptians (*see* no. 11). These scenes, painted or executed in painted relief, are found in the private tombs as early as the Third Dynasty, but evidence for their use in royal monuments has been scanty and in some cases unexpected. Such is the case of fragments from the Pyramid Temple of Weserkaf at Saqqara. Among others, there is a boating scene accompanied by running soldiers. But most interesting of all is the scene from which this fragment comes. Enough other fragments were preserved to enable the late William Stevenson Smith to reconstruct the scene as the trapping of birds in an orchard. In the upper right-hand corner of this fragment is found the outer edge of the clapnet used to catch the birds. The birds themselves have been identified as orioles, and a fragment from the same scene preserved the black and yellow colours of another oriole. As Smith has pointed out, we may expect to see such subjects as the king participating in what amounted to ritual events like the spearing of fish or harpooning of the hippopotamus. But bird-catching in an orchard seems unusual in a royal funerary temple. However, from the later Fifth Dynasty Sun Temple of Ne-user-Re at Abu Gurob there is a large body of material associating apparently private subjects with the changes of the seasons, represented in great detail in this temple. The Abu Gurob temple and its extensive decoration have been taken as evidence of an increasing devotion to the cult of the sun god Ra during the Fifth Dynasty and Smith says about the decoration at Abu Gurob that it is '. . . a testimony to the life-giving force of the Sun God and was offered in praise of his creative powers'. The earlier royal temples have been so shattered that little evidence remains for a complete assessment of their decoration, but these fragments from Weserkaf and a few others suggest that an essential aspect of the temple decoration was a more or less detailed catalogue, encyclopedia even, of the life of the land, reflecting the glory of the sun god and, at the same time, providing a perpetual supply of food offerings for the king in his temple. The temple scenes are therefore a more explicit statement of the intent behind the Mycerinus triads.

The tiny fragment is carved with exquisite detail. Like so much of the best relief of the Fourth and Fifth Dynasties, the work is almost more specifically drawing than sculpture. Even the markings, which are read as drawing lines, are in fact in relief. The birds are apparently engaging in a playful conflict. The colours of the birds are lost, but the branches retain some green and the fragment of the outer edge of the clapnet is black.

From Saqqara, Pyramid Temple of Weserkaf, Fifth Dynasty, painted limestone, width 15 cm., height 14.5 cm.

BIBLIOGRAPHY: *5000 Years Catalogue*, London, no. 34, pl. V; Smith, *Art and Architecture*, fig. 31, and pp. 68–9; W. S. Smith, *Interconnections in the Ancient Near East*, figs. 181–2, pp. 145–6.

COMMENTS: In his last work, *Interconnections*, Smith gave a masterful interpretation of the problem of the origin of such scenes in royal temples (pp. 141 ff.). The remarkable, encyclopedic nature of the Abu Gurob reliefs and their parallels in Weserkaf and elsewhere is enriched at Abu Gurob especially by the detailed labelling of birds and beasts by name, function and habits, such as their migrations. These inscriptions were studied by Edel: Smith gives the references, *ibid.* Weserkaf, the first king of the Fifth Dynasty, built a Sun Temple at Abusir (see no. 9).

E.L.B.T.

9 Head of King Weserkaf

Journal d'Entrée 90220

The identification of this head is based principally on its excavation in the Sun Temple of Weserkaf at Abusir, north of Saqqara. Despite its having been broken rudely from a statue, the head and crown have suffered little damage; even the nose is almost untouched. The face has that full, rather fatty modelling typical of the Fifth Dynasty and found also in the Fourth Dynasty (*e.g.* no. 7). The modelling is, however, schematic and lacks the specific detail found, for instance, in the faces of the Mycerinus triad. Nevertheless, the nostrils are treated with careful naturalism and the fatty tissue under the chin is well shown. Furthermore, the bulge between the root of the nose and the brow is prominent. In keeping with the general quality of the modelling, the details of the eyes are carved in relief, including the curious cosmetic lines which are characteristic of Egyptian art. The relief brows widen slightly at their ends. The lower lid of the left eye is in relief, while the right is not. This oversight is unexpected in such a highly finished work. The lips are chiselled to a fine edge and are not, as one might expect, outlined in relief. Faint traces of the chisel are still visible above the right corner of the upper lip. The philtrum is as sharply chiselled as the outline of the mouth. The lower lip is particularly full.

The king wears the Red Crown of Lower Egypt. The uraeus is not indicated. The crown is fitted closely around the ears. On the back, a broken space indicates the presence originally of the tall upright element characteristic of the Red Crown. Since it usually rises directly from the top of the crown, the vertical break may indicate the location of a narrow back pillar supporting the mass of the crown. There is no way of knowing if the head comes from a seated or standing statue.

Handled by an inexpert artist, the addition of so cumbersome an element as the crown might have been absurd. The Egyptian sculptor, however, has utilized the crown here as an integral aspect of the mass of the sculpture, and it is all the more to be regretted that the missing parts have not been recovered.

From Abusir, Sun Temple of Weserkaf, Fifth Dynasty, greywacke, height, life-size.

Bibliography: Lange and Hirmer, *Egypt*, pls. 48, 49; *ILN*, 230, no. 6149 (April 13, 1957), 578; other references *Annual Bibliog.* 1958, no. 58516.

COMMENTS: It has been suggested that the head belongs to a statue of the goddess Neith (*cf.* Lange and Hirmer, *op. cit.*, p. 411), who wears a similar crown. With the exception of group statues such as the Mycerinus triads, there are no statues of goddesses in the Old Kingdom, and it is not clear why such a statue should appear in a sun temple. On the other hand, it must be noted that there is no uraeus. From Weserkaf's Pyramid Temple at Saqqara comes a colossal red granite head of the king (*J. d'E.* 52501: *HESPOK*, p. 46 and pl. 17, a; *Manuel* III, pp. 29–30, pl. 7, 6). The modelling of the colossal head is even more reserved, while retaining the rotundity of the smaller head. The philtrum, so sharply defined in the Abusir head, is scarcely indicated in the Saqqara head; and the relief brows of the latter are less accentuated than the former. The Saqqara head wears the *nemes* headcloth, with the uraeus placed on the upper edge of the headband.

E.L.B.T.

10 RANOFER, HIGH PRIEST OF MEMPHIS

Catalogue général 19

The Priest of Ptah of Memphis, Ranofer, stands in the classical attitude of Egyptian sculpture. The head is alert; the arms hang close to the sides; the left leg and foot step forward slightly. The chest and arm muscles are tight and strong, and the statue is meant to represent Ranofer in youthful maturity. The legs, on the other hand, have that almost geometric schematic quality which is found throughout Egyptian art when the sculptor took particular pains to represent skeletal and muscular structure (*cf.* no. 7). The grooved hair is common in the Fifth Dynasty but is treated here with particular care, and the proportions are more realistic than usual. The treatment of the eyes is exceptional in the attention given to them in a private sculpture. Although the contours are executed in relief, there is a subtle plasticity in the upper lid and brow. In this respect, the sculpture is more closely related to that of Mycerinus (no. 7) than it is to the head of Weserkaf (no. 9), who is nearly contemporary with Ranofer. The somewhat pointed chin and slightly pursed lips (with outlines in relief) are distinctive and differ from the usual Fifth Dynasty type which tends to show a more prominent development of fatty tissues. The well-proportioned, rather broad shoulders are typical of the best sculpture of the time at both Giza and Saqqara.

The statue stands on a rectangular base and against a slab as wide as the sculpture itself. The base is inscribed with Ranofer's name and titles. As in the Chephren (no. 6) and Mycerinus (no. 7) sculptures, the base and back slab serve to emphasize the essentially cubic quality of the sculpture and its origin in the quarried block from which it was carved. Yet, incongruously in the Ranofer statue, the back slab ends at the middle of the head, which stands free above it.

The hands hold the short cylinders which have been defined as emblematic staves. When using wood, the Egyptian artist did not hesitate to build legs, arms, or staves in free air. On the other hand, the sculptor was quite able to do the same with stone if he wished, and did so rarely. Therefore, it seems evident that, once primitive inhibitions about the strength of stone had been conquered, the artist retained an instinctive fidelity to his medium: the limbs of wood sculptures might be disposed at will, in stone they retain the integrity of the block; and stones of differing hardnesses lent themselves to varying degrees of modelling.

Ranofer wears the short kilt favoured for the representation of the youthful man. The overlapping right side only is pleated. The royal kilt, on the other hand, is almost always pleated throughout, and has a tab

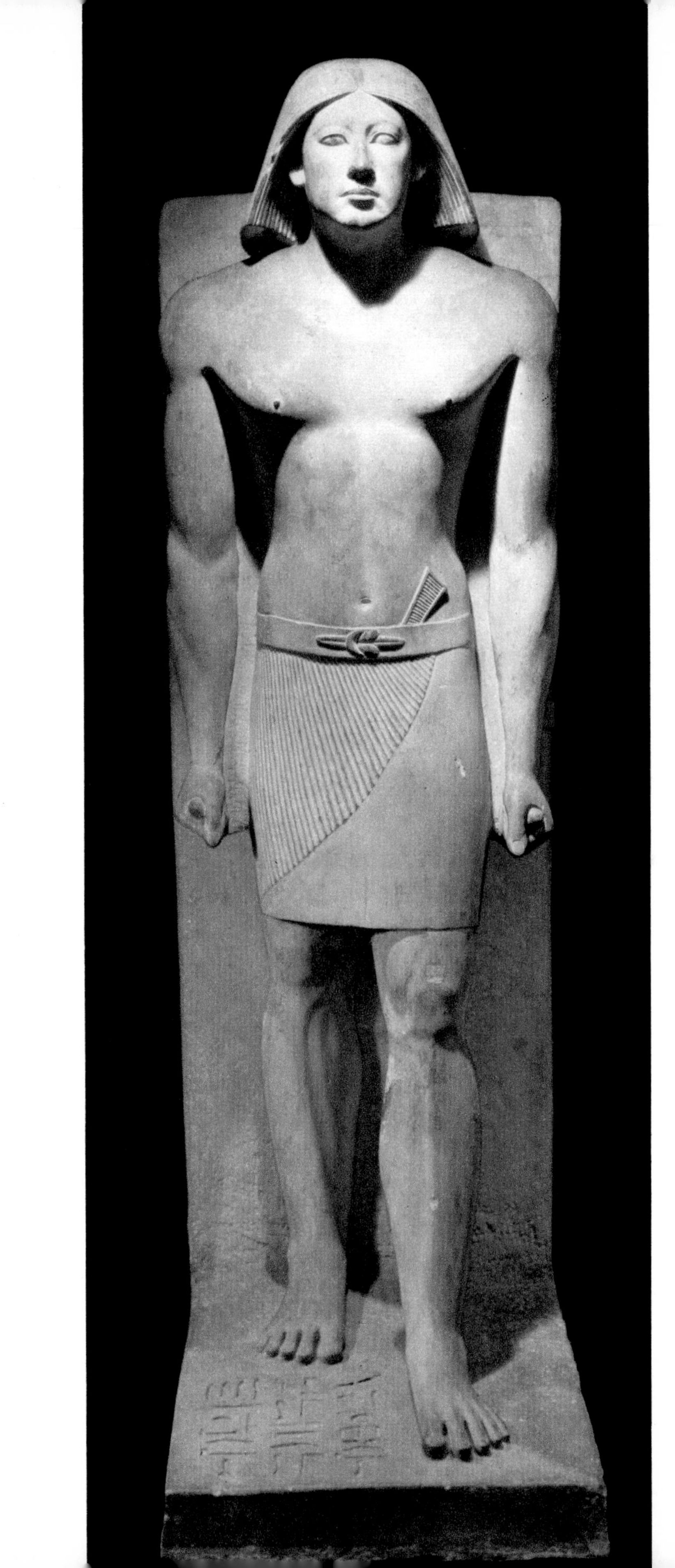

which extends between the legs (*cf.* no. 7). Furthermore, the underfold of royal kilts is almost always on the right side. The pleated end of Ranofer's kilt is pulled up from under the belt and, like the knot of the belt, is carved in relief. Faint traces of a painted broad collar remain on the breast. The collar is greyish, with red vertical zig-zag patterns (see Comments, no. 5). Some red is preserved here and there on the body.

From Saqqara (MM C 5), early Fifth Dynasty, painted limestone (nose restored), height 1 m. 80 cm.

BIBLIOGRAPHY: *PM* III, pp. 110–11; Smith, *HESPOK*, p. 49 and pl. 18, d; Vandier, *Manuel* III, pp. 119–24 and pl. 18, 2; *Tel*, pls. 23–5; Lange and Hirmer, *Egypt*, pls. 53, 56, 57. Kodansha, pls. 12, 13 (colour).

COMMENTS: For a full discussion of this statue with its contemporaries *cf.* Smith, *op. cit.*, and Vandier, *op. cit.* The head of *Cat. gén.* 18, a second life-sized statue of Ranofer, shows clearly a slight pouch beneath the eyes as well as a tendency towards corpulence in the torso and abdomen; these features, together with a relatively long kilt and the absence of any wig, indicate that it complements the other statue as a representation of more mature age; for the pairing of youth and age *cf.* two statues of a near-contemporary of Ranofer named Khnum-baf, excavated by the Museum of Fine Arts and now in the Metropolitan Museum of Art (*Apollo*, Sept. 1965, pp. 170–71, and Smith, *HESPOK*, pl. 19, c). The interesting rule that royal kilts have their overlap from the left side (*cf.* nos. 6, 7, 22, even 36) is belied curiously by no. 23. The splendid modelling of *Cat. gén.* 19 is especially well produced in *Tel*, pls. 23–25, and Lange and Hirmer, *Egypt*, pls. 56, 57. A large seated statue of Ranofer's wife was also found in the tomb (*Cat. gén.* 53); it is too damaged to know if it achieved the high standard of her husband's statues.

E.L.B.T.

11 A Boat Tournament

Catalogue général 1535

In all the varied repertory of Old and Middle Kingdom scenes of daily life, designed to perpetuate the existence of the tomb owner on the walls of his offering chapel, there is no other subject that offered the artist so many possibilities for interrelated action as the boat tournament. And of the numerous examples that have survived—every one of them slightly different—there is none that so well illustrates his sensitivity to composition and space. Most of the boatmen wield long poles with a forked end, and are punting, thrusting at their opponents, or preparing to deliver an overhand blow. At two points there is a convergence of wrestling figures, and a headlock is applied in both cases; one of these groups is further complicated by a fallen figure who is pushed by the pole of one man while his ankle is seized by another.

The overall movement of the action is from right to left, following the same direction in which the papyrus skiffs are moving; it begins with the converging poles of the two men at the right, is carried down and then upward by the fallen man and the punting figure above him, then onward to the second pair of wrestlers; its impetus is finally checked by the vertically crisscrossed poles of the two men at the extreme left. The accompanying sketch shows how imaginatively the attitudes have been combined, and how effectively the action has been integrated. It is unfortunate, however, that the painter has somewhat obscured the skill of the draughtsman and sculptor by giving the interlocked combatants a uniformly reddish-brown skin instead of varying the hue, as was sometimes done when overlapping figures were represented. In any case, however, the draughtsman has perhaps gone a little too far in interlacing the figures of the right-hand group. The modern spectator may also be perplexed by the fact that the poles pass behind the backs of the men who thrust them whenever the figures face left; to the ancient Egyptian this was an entirely acceptable combination of front and rear views, as explained in the description of Khai-bau-Sokar's reliefs (no. 5).

The locale of the tournament is evidently a marshy backwater or pond, to judge from the abundance of white and blue lotus plants that fill the water. As in other examples, the papyrus skiffs are laden with sacks containing some kind of fruit. The motivation of the combat is uncertain, but Vandier is probably right in attributing it to some sort of haphazard provocation. The cries that accompany these scenes show that the disputants are very much in earnest. One of them, at the left, cries: 'How's that? Thou'rt falling onto the field!' The man on the prow of the second boat shouts: 'Open him in his noggin!' and the man on

the first boat, who holds his assailant in a headlock with one arm, is apparently beating him with the other, for he says: 'His back is being hacked.' The remaining phrase is unexplained.

All but two of the men are slim and wear dapper short wigs. The remaining two are heavier and partially bald, as is more usually the case in other examples of the same scene.

The incomplete upper register shows fish being removed from wicker traps, and, at the right, being cut open for drying or baked whole upon a spit.

From Saqqara, exact provenance unrecorded, Fifth Dynasty, painted limestone, length 145 cm.

BIBLIOGRAPHY: Borchardt, *Denkmäler* (*Catalogue général*) I, 236–7. Texts: Adolf Erman, *Reden, Rufe und Lieder auf Gräberbildern des alten Reiches* (*Abhandlungen der Preussischen Akademie*, Ph.-hist. Kl. 15), p. 58. Upper register: Pierre Lacau, *Bulletin de l'Institut Français d'Archéologie Orientale au Caire* 54 (1954), 137–63. Comparative material: Vandier, *Manuel* V, 510–31 and 549–51; Kodansha, pl. 30 (colour).

H.G.F.

12 SENEB AND HIS FAMILY

Journal d'Entrée 51281

The dwarf was a favourite subject of the Egyptian artist and is often found in the reliefs of the Fifth and Sixth Dynasties. Rarely is the dwarf represented in sculpture in the round, and this group is unique in presenting a dwarf with his family: wife, son and daughter, all of whom show normal physical development. Although the wife's embrace is perfectly conventional, there is something particularly touching in this representation. The compactness of the sculpture is exceptional in its treatment of the complex group, and in this connection we can do no better than to quote the late William Stevenson Smith:

> By making the head large in proportion to the body he has given the upper part of the seated figure the same height as that of the wife, but has fashioned the arms small and placed them on the breast with the hands laid over one another. . . . In front are placed a pair of small figures, naked son and daughter, which occupy the space which the legs of an ordinary man would have filled. Thus the sculptor has created the same impression, in the disposition of his masses, that would have been presented by an ordinary seated figure.

All the figures, the parents especially, wear that smiling countenance particularly typical of the Fifth Dynasty (not evident, however, in the statue of Ranofer, no. 10). The eyes are treated plastically rather than in relief. There is a minimum of modelling throughout the figures, although the somewhat flabby abdomen of the dwarf is discreetly suggested. The lady wears a long garment which was originally painted; the details of the upper part of the dress are now missing. She wears bracelets which are indicated in relief. A heavy wig covers her own hair, a little of which, parted in the centre, appears below the wig. Seneb's hair is cropped short, and he wears the usual kilt. Both children are naked, although the boy sports the youth's side lock. Originally the male bodies were red, although it would appear that the boy might have been a lighter colour. Much of the original red remains on Seneb himself. His wife and daughter bear no trace of their original colour, which should have been yellow. The hair of the parents is black.

Among other offices, Seneb held priesthoods in the funerary cults of two Fourth Dynasty kings, Ra-djedef and Cheops. The names of the children are compounded with these royal names.

See also Colour Plate III.

From Giza, Sixth Dynasty, painted limestone, height 33 cm.

BIBLIOGRAPHY: H. Junker, *Giza* V, pp. 3 ff., frontispiece and pl. 9; Smith, *HESPOK*, p. 57; Vandier, *Manuel* III, pp. 80, 132, pl. 48, 5; Kodansha, pl. 22 (colour).

COMMENTS: For other dwarfs, see Smith, *op. cit.*, pp. 57 f., and pl. 25, d. The most famous is the standing figure of a man named Khnum-hotpe, *Manuel* III, pl. 18, 1. Other publications of dwarfs include *ASAE* 38 (1938), 286 ff., pls. XXXV ff.; and a lady dwarf attendant in the tomb of Nebet, a queen of Unas (end of the Fifth Dynasty), *ASAE* 40 (1940), pl. LXXIX.

E.L.B.T

13 JEWELLERY OF THE PRINCESS KHNUMET

Catalogue général 52975–52979

While Twelfth Dynasty craftsmen generally followed older traditions in producing objects of chased and inlaid gold, bringing these techniques to a level of perfection never excelled in later times, they also borrowed foreign techniques and motifs. Granulation was used by the Sumerians at Ur in the middle of the third millennium BC, about five centuries before the Minoans or Egyptians are known to have adopted it. In the jewellery of Khnumet, the daughter of Amenemhet II, it is exploited to a remarkable degree, for this style of decoration did not become really popular in the Nile Valley until the end of the Eighteenth Dynasty.

Most unusual of all, however, is a circular pendant that contains a painting of a couchant bull or cow, with one foreleg folded under the animal, the other extended; this is applied either to the backing, which appears to be a combination of plaster and blue frit, or to the underside of the crystal disk that protects it. While the motif is purely Egyptian, the technique has been compared to a painted fragment of crystal of somewhat later date (about the beginning of the New Kingdom) that was found at Knossos and represents a charging bull in Minoan style.

The five pendants attached to the medallion show a basic pattern (⌑) that is again most closely paralleled at Knossos in the decoration of a gaming board only slightly earlier than the New Kingdom.

The motifs of the other pendants—stylized flies, a butterfly, shells and a five-pointed star—are not wholly foreign to Egypt. Flies are often found among Middle Kingdom amulets, but are usually more naturalistic than these. The butterfly, conversely, occurs more frequently as an independent motif in Crete than it does in Egypt, but the form is too naturalistic to be considered a Minoan creation. Shell pendants are exceedingly common in the Middle Kingdom, but they are not usually grooved, as in the present case, nor are both valves shown. The star is Egyptian in style, with five points and a circular centre; but the number of points, and their thickness, would also be appropriate to a starfish, as would the spiny-looking granulation and the presence of the adjacent cockles. Whatever may have inspired them, it is evident that the butterfly and star show the same technique as the circular pendants; the outlines are constructed of wire and the space between is filled with one or more rows of gold granules. Since the butterfly has a sliding clasp on the back, this pendant is necessarily backed with a sheet of gold. The cockles are hollow. In all cases the chains show a complex single or double columnar type of construction.

The two dozen hollow gold birds are the most puzzling part of the group. They are evidently represented as though viewed from the back, the underside being flat. The details of the wings and tail are roughly indicated with leaflike striations and the size of the eye is extremely exaggerated. Two holes at either side of the tail, and virtually at the very end of it, provide the means of attachment. It has been assumed that the birds must have been sewn to the princess's clothing or hair. Even so, they could hardly remain upright, and if placed beak downwards they would still swing free, and would in either case face left, contrary to the expected orientation (*cf.* nos. 1 and 19). Odd as it may seem, one must therefore consider the possibility that they were suspended from their tails. There is no parallel for these birds at all events, and it can only be said that they are totally un-Egyptian in style.

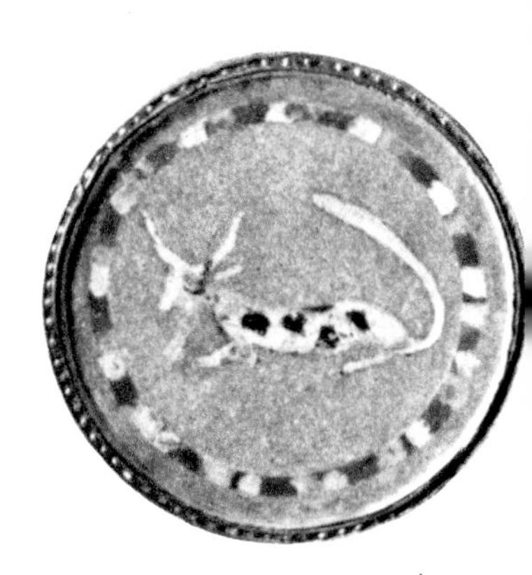

It must also be pointed out that the bull or cow on the crystal-covered medallion likewise faces left. If the painting was done on the back of the crystal, however, this anomaly might perhaps be explained by the painter's unfamiliarity with the technique. Possibly he lost sight of the fact that the animal would be reversed when mounted.

See also Colour Plate II.

From Dahshur, the tomb of Khnumet, adjacent to the pyramid of Amenemhet II, mid-Twelfth Dynasty, all gold except for the gold-framed frit medallion with crystal cover; diameter of crystal medallion (group *Cat. gén.* 52975) 2 cm.; length of flies (group 52976) 1.5 cm.; width of butterfly (group 52977) 2.7 cm.; max. width of stars (group 52978) 2.5 cm.; height of birds (group 52979) 1.1 cm.

BIBLIOGRAPHY: de Morgan *Fouilles à Dahchour* II, pp. 65–8 and pl. 12; L. Keimer, *ASAE* 34 (1934), 195–6, 203, and pl. 16 (1); G. Möller, *Die Metallkunst der alten Aegypter*, 28 ff.; A. Lucas and Guy Brunton, *ASAE* 36 (1936), 197–200; P. E. Newberry, *JEA* 6 (1920), 159 and pl. 16, and *JEA* 24 (1938), 126–7; E. Vernier, *La bijouterie et la joaillerie égyptiennes* (*MFIAO* 2 [1907]), pp. 94–5, 127 and pls. 1 (13–15), 15 (2); and *Bijoux et orfèvreries* (*Cat. gén.*), 320–23 and pl. 73; M. Vilímková, *Egyptian Jewellery*, p. 24 and pl. 17; Madeleine Trokay, *Chron. d'Eg.* 43 (1968), 271–80 and fig. 1.

COMMENTS: Möller seems to have been the first to compare the Minoan gaming board, for which see A. Evans, *Palace of Minos* I, pl. 5 and fig. 338; the painted crystal is shown *ibid.*, III, pl. 19. Of equal significance is the fact that one of the most spectacular examples of Minoan granulation, a pair of gold hornets dated to about 2000 BC, has three pendant rimmed disks (Marinatos, *Crete and Mycenae*, pl. 13). Disk pendants of this kind are foreign to Egypt, although, like the granulated technique, they are known much earlier in Mesopotamia (C. L. Wooley, *Ur Excavations* II, pl. 133; granulation, pls. 151, 152); for the origins of granulation see also Trokay. The motif ⊡ is not very common in Egypt except as it emerges in a pattern of interlocking circles (Old and Middle Kingdom patterns on clothing, Cairo *Cat. gén.* 55,274, J. Quibell, *El Kab*, pl. 5 [1]; Kerma faience of Late Middle Kingdom, Smith, *Art and Architecture*, pl. 80 B [top right]; New Kingdom ceilings, Jéquier, *Decoration Égyptienne*, pls. 14, 15, 33), and is rarely independent (Twelfth Dynasty clay sealing, W. F. M. Petrie *et al.*, *Lahun* II, pl. 64 [255]; decoration on faience hippopotami, L. Keimer, *Rev. de l'Egypte ancienne* 2 [1929], pp. 210 ff., figs. 8–11, 13, 15, 48; and *cf.* the pattern of Middle Kingdom cushions, Jéquier, *Frises d'objets*, pp. 238–9).

Lucas and Brunton discuss the crystal, pointing out both the Minoan parallel and two later Egyptian examples of miniature painting overlaid with this form of volcanic glass, on a chair and earring of

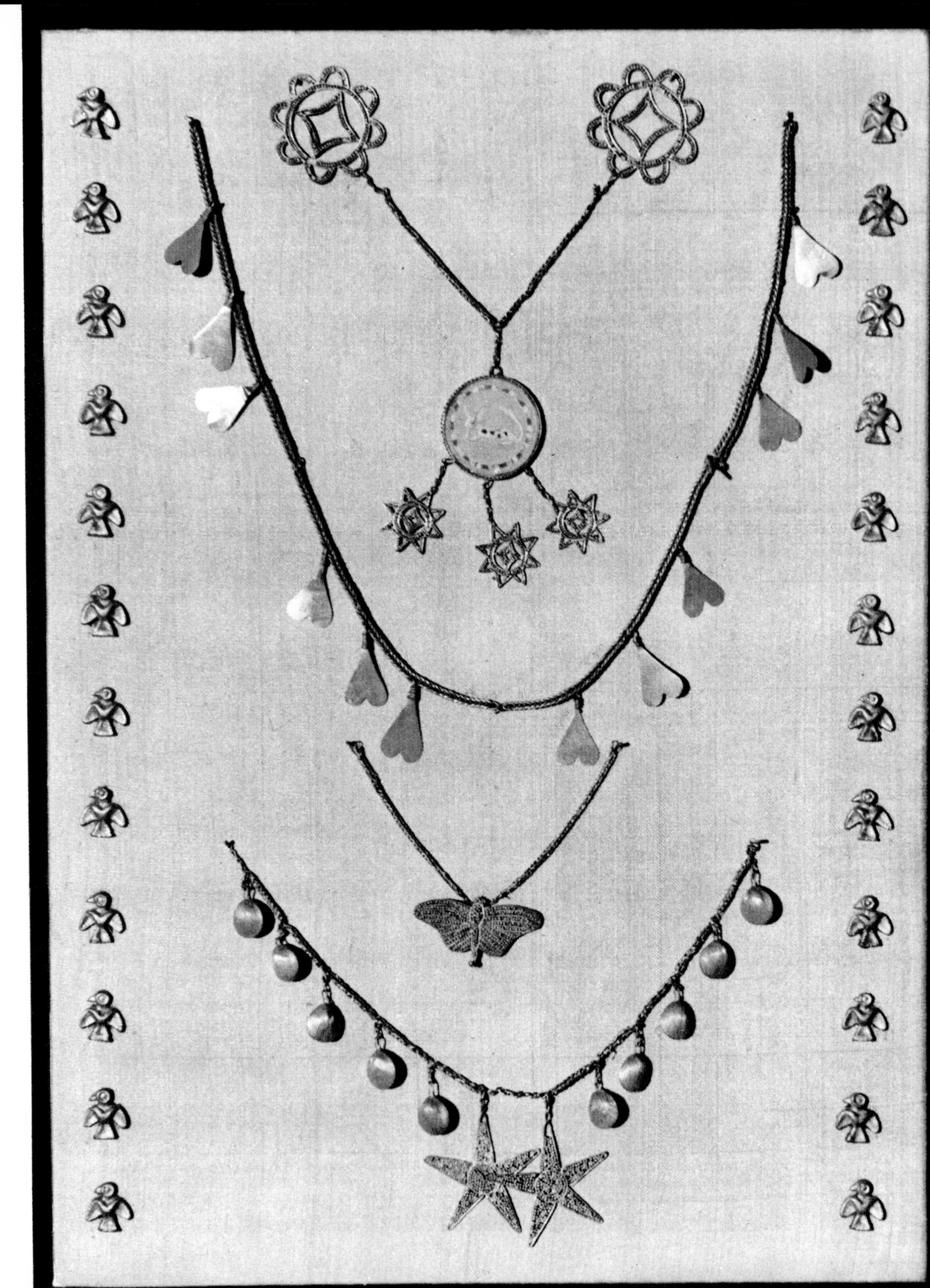

Tut-ankh-Amun. Keimer offers an interesting comparison of butterflies in Minoan and Egyptian art and Vernier (*La bijouterie*, 94–5) explains the structure of the single and double columnar type of chains. For some examples of Middle Kingdom fly-amulets see G. Brunton, *Qau and Badari* I, pl. 48 (36), II, pl. 97 (36), III, pl. 4 (22), and *Matmar*, pl. 31 (49–52). Egyptian star pendants are rare, but see the faience amulet in G. Brunton, *Mostagedda*, pl. 76 (Second Intermediate Period) and an Eighteenth Dynasty starlike flower(?) with seven points and a large boss at the centre (H. E. Winlock, *Treasure of Three Egyptian Princesses*, p. 25 and pl. 12).

H.G.F.

14 Statue of Queen Nofret

Catalogue général 381

Framed by the tubular tresses of a massive wig, and surmounted by the royal cobra, the sightless gaze of Queen Nofret has lost none of its majesty, scarcely impaired by the loss of the inlaid eyes and the nose. The strength of her face is established almost geometrically by the curved edge of the facets beneath the eyes, and by a tautness that frames the space between the corners of the mouth and the chin. Viewed from below, the line of the mouth seems almost straight, but at eye level it assumes a prescient smile. The curve of the eyebrows, in definite relief, is in keeping with the bold treatment of the wig.

The Queen's body is sculptured with great restraint, its gently curved forms relieved by the horizontal line of the upraised left forearm. This line reinforces the horizontal folds at the waist and knee of the seated figure, and is echoed by the line of the clavicular prominences below the neck. The sculptor has only very lightly traced such details as the upper edge of the dress, the shoulder straps, a pectoral suspended from a broad ribbon, and a pair of bracelets. The pattern of these accessories is very similar to that of the finery shown in a relief from Bersha dating to the next reign (no. 15). In both cases, the pendant has a trapezoidal form that is more elongated than any of the several Twelfth Dynasty pectorals that have survived, but recalls the tasselled ornaments that appear on Old Kingdom statuary. Like most of the contemporary pectorals, however, that of Nofret features a royal cartouche—the cartouche of Sesostris II. This is flanked by cobras wearing the crowns of Upper Egypt (right) and Lower Egypt (left). The lower register shows a pair of *wedjat*-eyes (human eyes with pendant markings emblematic of the god Horus: 𓂀) and, at the bottom, a djed-pillar (𓊽), symbolizing stability and permanence, flanked by a pair of lapwings representing the common people of Egypt (𓅚).

In contrast to the lightly traced clothing and jewellery, the form and structure of the wig emerge all the more emphatically. Although it is sometimes called the 'Hathorian' wig, it is not known to be associated with that goddess prior to its appearance in this statue and in a similar one representing the same queen. It is true, however, that it continues to appear on Hathorian columns and sistra long after the end of the Middle Kingdom, when it otherwise falls into disuse. And the wig itself apparently has an archaic prototype. Nofret's statue (and its counterpart) provides the clearest example of its structure. Its undulating surface and incised longitudinal striations represent wavy hair that is bound at intervals by horizontal bands

that determine the shape of the thick tresses. The ends curve around a disklike weight that is probably made of carnelian (*cf.* no. 15). At the rear, from the point where the lateral tresses are parted, a straight mass of hair falls downward to approximately the same length, where it encounters a supporting back pillar that continues on down to the curved back of the seat. The Queen's ears are spread out by the wig in a manner that is characteristic of the Twelfth Dynasty. Just in front of each ear a crescent-shaped curl of her own hair is visible.

Much of the lower part of the statue is restored, as well as both elbows. The head and torso were found by Mariette at Tanis in the winter of 1860–61 and the lower section came to light in 1904. A second statue from Tanis evidently accompanied this one, although it is now generally conceded that both were transported there in antiquity from another site. Its face has suffered an equal amount of damage, the arms even more so, but it may be seen that both hands were placed palm downward on the knees. It has been

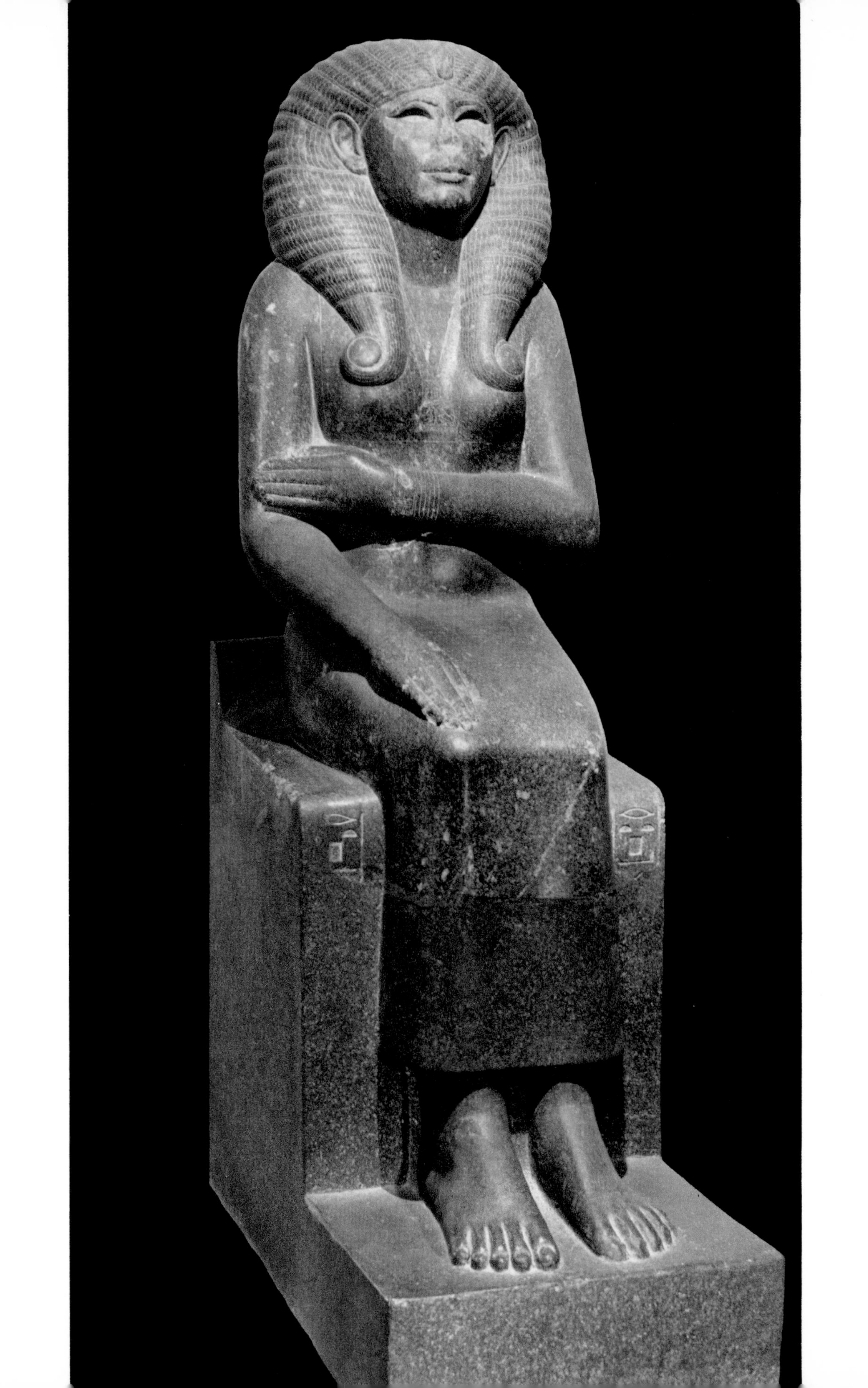

suggested that the statue shown here was balanced by yet another that showed the right arm raised. This gesture seems, however, to be confined to the left arm in Middle Kingdom statuary, and in any case the asymmetry of the two existing figures would not have been offensive to Egyptian taste if they had been paired—quite the contrary. Such variations are common in nearly every period, and a certain degree of asymmetry is usual even in the faces of the finest statues, where it was doubtless felt to impart a certain liveliness to the features. In the present case, for example, there is a very noticeable difference in the shape and level of the eyebrows.

The second statue provides the Queen's complete titulary, identifying her as the consort of Sesostris II, a king's daughter and 'mistress of all women'.

From Tanis, reign of Sesostris II, black granite, height 112 cm., height as restored 165 cm.

BIBLIOGRAPHY: Borchardt, *Statuen* II, pp. 1–2 and pl. 60; W. von Bissing, *Denkmäler ägyptischen Skulptur*, pls. 21, 22 and text; H. G. Evers, *Staat aus dem Stein*, pls. 74, 75; C. Aldred, *Middle Kingdom Art*, pl. 44 and p. 46; Bodil Hornemann, *Types of Ancient Egyptian Statuary*, no. 1067; Smith, *Art and Architecture*, pl. 67; Walther Wolf, *Die Kunst Ägyptens*, fig. 255 and pp. 320–21; Vandier, *Manuel* III, pp. 183, 222, 257–8 and pl. 74 (3); Kodansha, pl. 37 (colour).

COMMENTS: For the archaic prototype of the wig see Smith, *op. cit.*, p. 27 and pl. 12; the Hathorian adaptation of this is exemplified by the inlay on a box dating to Amenemhet III (H. E. Winlock, *Treasure of Lahun*, p. 15, fig. 3), by a column represented in a tomb dating to his predecessor (A. Blackman, *Meir* VI, pl. 11) and actual columns that are probably of the same date (L. Habachi, *Tell Basta*, pp. 61–67 and pls. 18–20); *cf.* the similar example in Boston, W. S. Smith, *Ancient Egypt*, 1960, fig. 46. Vandier (*ibid.*, p. 257) cites a non-royal example of the wig that may well go back to the reign of Sesostris I (Metropolitan Museum of Art 33.1.5–6). The second statue of Nofret (Cairo *Cat. gén.* 382) is almost identical to the first apart from the different position of the left arm, but the eyes show the prolongation of the 'cosmetic line' in relief, which makes them look smaller, and the pectoral shows the cartouche flanked by a pair of vultures on hieroglyphs representing 'gold'. The presence of the lapwings in the pectoral of the first statue is perhaps to be explained by reading the entire group 'the commoners behold the stability of the King of Upper and Lower Egypt Khakheperre'.

A much smaller version of Nofret is a black granite bust in Boston, see Terrace in *BMFA* 66 (1968), 22–3, fig. 23, and *The Connoisseur*, August 1968, p. 269, fig. 9.

H.G.F.

15 Relief from the Tomb of Djehuty-hotpe

Journal d'Entrée 30199

The tomb chapel of Djehuty-hotpe, nomarch of the Fifteenth Province of Upper Egypt, was built in the reign of Sesostris III and, together with that of Ukh-hotpe, his contemporary neighbour in the Fourteenth Province (no. 16), it represents the culmination of Twelfth Dynasty workmanship. Some time after it was built an earthquake caused a subsidence of the rock strata in the cliffs from which the tomb was hollowed, destroying the portico and fragmenting much of the decoration on the left-hand wall of the inner chamber. Of the several fragments that have been removed to the Cairo Museum, London, and Boston this one best illustrates the restrained elegance of the figures and the finesse of the painted relief.

Carved in crisp relief and deftly painted, three of Djehuty-hotpe's several daughters stand in a row before him, each one sniffing a long-stemmed blossom of the fragrant blue lotus. Their yellow-brown faces and limbs are lightly edged with a thin line of red that accents the details of the nostrils, philtrum and lips as well as the slight projection at the elbow of the straightened arm. The slender bodies are sheathed in the traditional long white dress, with shoulder straps that only partially cover the breasts. Despite the fact that only one curving tress is shown, their coiffure is probably the same as the one worn by Queen Nofret (no. 14); the wavy hair is similarly shaped by means of horizontal bands and is weighted by a disk that is probably made of carnelian. The first wears a fillet decked with blossoms of the blue lotus, while the second prefers the white lotus, the petals of which are fuller and rounder, although less pleasantly scented. In all cases the flowers are painted with extraordinary delicacy. The band of the fillet seems to be made of green rushwork with blue and white binding and braided edging, but it is possible that this represents a more durable material such as faience beadwork. A similar pattern appears in one of the two bracelets and anklets that appear on each limb, and in the long band from which a pectoral is suspended. The pectoral is probably made of gold openwork, inlaid with faience or semiprecious stones. A multicoloured frame encloses a sun disk flanked by two cobras, above which is a conical object that Bissing describes as an inverted flower. Two Lower Egyptian crowns (𓋔) appear at the top of this group. For an unexplained reason, perhaps simply because of their distinctive shape, Lower Egyptian crowns, but not Upper Egyptian ones (𓋑) were a popular motif in the Middle Kingdom; they occur singly, as pendant amulets, and in pairs, as part of the design on the underside of scarabs.

Another fragment in the Cairo Museum supplements the remnants of inscription at the top, which describes each of the first two girls as 'his beloved daughter, who does what he praises every day'; one is called Sit-hedj-hotpe, and the other Sit-kheperka. Both are 'theophoric' names, the second referring to Kheperkare Sesostris I, who lived three generations earlier.

See also Colour Plate IV.

From Bersha, the tomb of Djehuty-hotpe, reign of Sesostris III, painted limestone, height 80 cm.

Bibliography: P. E. Newberry *El Bersheh* I, frontispiece and pl. 29; W. von Bissing, *Denkmäler ägyptischer Sculptur*, pl. 35 and text; Jéquier, *Frises d'objets*, p. 46 (fig. 114); W. S. Smith, *AJA* 55 (1951), pp. 321–2 and fig. 1, and *Art and Architecture*, pl. 74. Kodansha, pl. 38 (colour).

Comments: Bissing notes a few other examples of the wrinkled elbow; this also occurs at Meir (A. Blackman, *Meir* II, pl. 14). The fillet with upright lotus blossoms is most closely paralleled by one worn by the wife of Ibu on a fragment from his tomb (H. Steckeweh, *Fürstengräber von Qâw*, pl. 15); the blossoms look more like actual flowers than the stylized floral motifs applied to diadems of the Middle Kingdom, and resemble the improvised fillets of Old Kingdom boatmen (see Ebba Kerrn, *Acta Orientalia* 24 [1959], 161–88). The two species of lotus are discussed by W. D. Spalton, *Ancient Egypt* 1917, 1–20. For the Lower Egyptian crown as an amulet see G. Brunton, *Qau and Badari* I, pl. 48 (bottom left), II, pls. 98, 99 (63), and *Mostagedda*, pl. 57 (63), and *Matmar*, pl. 32 (90–92); for pairs of crowns on scarabs see W. M. F. Petrie, *Lahun* II, pls. 64 (265, 268, 271, 284, 294, 300), 65 (313), *Harageh*, pl. 20 (4, 5, 7), etc.

A large proportion of the decoration of Djehuty-hotpe's tomb consisted of painting alone, see Terrace, *Egyptian Paintings of the Middle Kingdom*, pls. XLIX–LI (watercolour copies by W. S. Smith). A fragment of painted relief from the tomb showing male attendants, now in Boston, is illustrated in Terrace, *BMFA* 60 (1968), 24–5, fig. 27.

H.G.F.

16 Group Statue of Ukh-hotpe

Catalogue général 459

During the later half of the Twelfth Dynasty, statuary becomes increasingly monumental in the literal sense of the word. The attitude of men is frequently as passive as that of women—in the majority of cases they no longer have one or both hands fisted, but hold their hands flat upon their lap or at their sides. A long kilt, adapted to the embonpoint of advancing years, is usual, or a voluminous cloak, and in either case a part of the resultant surface is inscribed with a column of text—in some cases even more than a column. Hard dark stone such as granite is preferred to the limestone that was so popular in the Old Kingdom and Early Middle Kingdom, a choice of material that lends itself to simplicity of form. These developments are related to an evolution in the use of statues, which were no longer deposited by the dozens in hidden chambers (*serdabs*) within tombs, but more frequently were displayed in the tomb chapels or in temples, where they could be seen, and read, by priests and other visitors.

In the case of Ukh-hotpe's monument, these developments are carried to a very logical extreme. The family group has been presented against a backing that not only has the form of a contemporary stela, but carries symbols that are appropriate to that kind of monument: at the top are a pair of eyes with falcon-markings that associate them with the god Horus; flanking these are the sedgelike plant of Upper Egypt (𓇓) and the papyrus that is emblematic of the Delta (𓇅). The group was placed in a statue niche at the back of a rock-cut tomb chapel on the west side of the Nile. The same group of emblems appears at the rear wall of the niche and in both cases the plant emblems were correctly oriented south and north.

Artistic convention has given the face of Ukh-hotpe something of the heavy-lidded sobriety of his ruler, Sesostris III, contributing further to the reserved and even sombre aspect of the group. But the bright clear colours of his painted tomb belie that impression, as do the sprightly female attendants who throng the scenes that ordinarily represent male occupations. It has been suggested that the emphasis on women may be explained by his position as overseer of the priesthood of the local goddess Hathor, but they surely reflect his own tastes as well, for his female companions include four wives and seven concubines. Polygamy is rare in ancient Egypt, and this exception is doubtless to be considered an imitation of royal custom that was intended to guarantee an heir to the throne, for there are several usurpations of royal iconography in Ukh-hotpe's chapel.

Only two wives and a pigtailed daughter are depicted here; from spectator's right to left they are Nub-kau, Nebhut-henutsen, and Khnum-hotpe. The women wear heavy wigs of the kind worn by Queen Nofret (no. 14). All the figures have large ears—another echo of royal physiognomy.

From tomb C1 at Meir, reign of Sesostris III, dark grey granite, height 31.5 cm.

BIBLIOGRAPHY: Borchardt, *Statuen* II, pp. 51–2; J. J. Vandier, *Revue d'Egyptologie* 13 (1961), 110–11; H. Fischer, *Kush* 9 (1961), p. 55, n. 17. For the tomb, see A. M. Blackman and M. R. Apted, *The Rock Tombs of Meir* VI and E. L. B. Terrace, *Egyptian Paintings of the Middle Kingdom*, pls. 47, 48.

COMMENTS: Vandier dates Ukh-hotpe's statue to the preceding reign of Sesostris II. Blackman says (*Meir* I, p. 13) that he 'flourished in the reigns of Sesostris II and III' and (*Meir* VI, 15) 'We are still of the opinion . . . that this tomb-chapel may date from the reign of Sesostris III. . . .' Everything seems to favour this opinion, including the physiognomy of the statue. For the niche in which the statue was placed see *ibid.*, pl. 16.

H.G.F.

17 Statue of Amenemhet III

Catalogue général 395

The king of Egypt, by virtue of his divine nature, was the link between men and the gods. He therefore appears as the sole officiant who, in temple reliefs and statuary, presents offerings to them and performs the other ceremonies of the daily ritual. In practice, these duties were delegated to priests who acted in his name, and who are sometimes seen to wear more or less distinctive regalia. Such appurtenances were not usually shared by the supreme pontiff, however, since his role is automatically proclaimed by any and all of his royal raiment. The present case is not only one of the few exceptions to this rule, but is by far the earliest, and the only one that is represented in statuary rather than in painting or relief.

Apart from the massive wig, the most conspicuous article of attire is the leopard skin that is thrown over the king's shoulders, with a forepaw appearing on one side and the head of the animal on the other; it is held in place by a double band, the loose ends of which fall obliquely downward. By the reign of Amenemhet III the leopard skin cloak had become an archaism that was restricted to priestly use; specifically it is the *setem*-priest that wears such a cloak from the Old Kingdom onward. In a very few paintings and reliefs of much later date (four to five centuries later), it is again worn by kings in a context that clearly indicates its priestly function.

The heavy necklace that hangs low on the king's chest is the *menit*, a ritual object that makes its first appearance towards the end of the Old Kingdom. It appears on a relief-representation of the same king from the temple south of his pyramid at Hawara, but is not attested in representations of other rulers, and is, in fact, most frequently associated with women, although priests of Hathor also wear it in the Middle and early New Kingdoms. During this period it terminates in two counterweights, which later are fused into one; both are at least partly visible at the back of the statue, below the wig. The main part of the necklace consists of numerous strands of tiny beads that are bunched together and suspended from a chain of larger beads, at the other end of which the two counterweights are attached.

The two falcon-headed standards that rest against each shoulder represent the god Horus either as the kingly god who is identified with the bearer, or as a god who is distinct from him and whom he serves as priest. Such standards occur again in the mid-Eighteenth Dynasty, and during the succeeding dynasty they become fairly common in both royal and private statuary, including some leopard-mantled priests.

These later examples display a variety of divinities, and there are scenes in relief showing the standards being presented by the king to the appropriate gods. In the present case the standards are probably to be identified with a Horus who was worshipped along with the crocodile-god Suchos in Amenemhet III's temple at Kiman Faris, near which the statue was found, but this god, at the same time, probably represents the king himself. It is more difficult to say whether the *menit*-necklace implies any association with Hathor, but it may be significant that a statue of this goddess was found in this king's temple south of the Hawara pyramid, where the fragment of relief also shows him wearing a *menit*.

The modelling of the face—and particularly the strongly muscled mouth—recalls the magnificent maned sphinx of the same ruler in the Cairo Museum, but here the features have a somewhat flatter, mask-like character that is in keeping with the statue's hieratic function. The wig, as Evers points out, lends structural emphasis; it retreats at the temples and its basic horizontal divisions correspond to the level of the eyes and mouth. The winding body of the uraeus cobra is visible at the top of the wig, but its head, which was probably made of metal, has disappeared.

The king's wig is unique. Its length is insufficient to associate it with the tripartite style of wig that is worn by gods, its shape broader, its structure more complex. The domed form of the upper part is produced by an emerging series of slender strands that partially cover the thicker outer strands and hold them in. The breadth and massiveness of it is very much in the style of Middle Kingdom wigs such as those worn by Queen Nofret (no. 14) and those belonging to a contemporary series of offering bearers. To find a prototype one must go back to the Archaic Period, as in the case of Nofret's coiffure.

The modelling of the torso is rather flat and simple, in keeping with the variety of regalia that is displayed upon it. The well-defined line of the slightly sagging pectorals resembles that of the offering bearers, who are traditionally corpulent. This feature, and the heavy lids, suggest that the statue represents the king in his later years.

From Mit Faris (Medinet el Fayum, ancient Shedyet); reign of Amenemhet III, grey granite, height 100 cm.

BIBLIOGRAPHY: *PM* IV, 99; Borchardt, *Statuen* II, p. 13 and pl. 64; W. von Bissing, *Denkmäler ägyptischer Sculptur*, pl. 30 and text; H. G. Evers, *Staat aus dem Stein*, pls. 127, 128 and §§ 701–4; Bodil Hornemann, *Types of Ancient Egyptian Statuary*, no. 362; C. Aldred, *Middle Kingdom Art in Egypt*, pl. 76 and p. 54; W. Westendorf, *Ancient Egypt*, 94; *Tel*, pl. 60; Vandier, *Manuel* III, 209–10; Kodansha, pl. 43 (colour).

COMMENTS: The form of the necklace led von Bissing to associate the statue with Khonsu, and Evers follows him in describing the king as priest of that god. Khonsu probably acquired this emblem from Ihy at a later date, on the basis of their both being sons—of Amun in one case and of Hathor in the other; for the same reason the *menit* was also added to the emblem of Nefertem, the son of Ptah. The king, as Horus, is also a son—the dutiful heir of Osiris—but it seems doubtful that this role would have led to an assimilation of Ihy's *menit* as early as the Twelfth Dynasty. In this connection it may be noted that the leopard skin would suit the role of filial piety, as exemplified by the youthful 'Pillar-of-his-Mother', another aspect of Horus (L. Habachi, *Tell Basta*, p. 14 and pl. 2). Westendorf, comparing the figure that precedes the king on the recto of the Narmer Palette, in fact takes both this figure and the statue under discussion

to represent the heir to the throne. But the filial aspect is not made explicit by the king's coiffure, which is quite different from the sidelock of youth. The skin-clad *setem*-priests of the Old and Middle Kingdom wear a shoulder-length wig, on the other hand, and it does not seem necessary to explain it as a Libyan feature, as Aldred suggests. The Old Kingdom evidence for the *menit* is given by E. Staehelin, *Untersuchungen zur ägyptischen Tracht im Alten Reich*, 125–7; *cf.* also H. Fischer, *Dendera*, p. 122 and n. 524. Middle Kingdom representations are illustrated and discussed by Jéquier, *Frises des objets*, 71–7; it appears on a priest of Hathor who is a contemporary of Amenemhet III (C. C. Edgar in *Le Musée Egyptien* III, p. 58 and pls. 33, 36); the relief fragment showing Amenemhet III wearing the *menit* is illustrated by W. F. M. Petrie, *Labyrinth, Harageh and Mazghuneh*, pl. 25. For the priestly use of the leopard skin by kings of the New Kingdom see Smith, *Art and Architecture*, pl. 141, A (Ay, in the tomb of Tut-ankh-Amun); A. Blackman, *The Temple of Derr*, pl. 41 (Ramesses II); Oriental Institute, *Medinet Habu* IV, pl. 230 (Ramesses III, on base of Amun's bark). The king's presentation of standards to the gods is shown *ibid.* V, pl. 330. For the presence of Horus in the temple of Amenemhet III see L. Habachi, *ASAE* 37 (1937), 85–95, and for Hathor see W. M. F. Petrie, *op. cit.*, pl. 24. Hermann Kees notes that Horus is the co-deity at Shedyet 'undoubtedly because of the exemplary benefactions of the rulers of Dynasty XII' (*Ancient Egypt: a Cultural Topography*, 225).

H.G.F.

18 Statue of Si-kahika

Journal d'Entrée 43928

Despite the fact that it is one of the most striking portrayals of old age that has survived from a period that is noted for its realistic treatment of this subject, the statue of Si-kahika is one of the least familiar masterpieces in the Cairo Museum. Egyptian sculpture was never entirely confined to the ideal of youthful vigour that generally predominated, but it was, in particular, the weary countenance of Sesostris III that, reflected in countless statues of his subjects, lent a degree of respectability to wrinkles and creases, and all the other accidents of old age. It is true that this degree of realism would probably not have entered into royal portraiture in the first place, if there had not been a concomitant change of mood. Another reflection of such a change may be the slight but unmistakable tendency towards passivity in late Twelfth Dynasty statuary (*cf.* no. 16). A standing statue of Sesostris III shows a ruler empty-handed for the first time, and his son, Amenemhet III is the first king who is known to sit with both hands flat upon his lap.

While the statue of Si-kahika shows the influence of these developments, the cheeks are more creased, the eyes more deeply hooded, the forehead more wrinkled than the corresponding features of any royal statue. Possibly this face actually mirrors an individual. In any case, it has an exceptional and compelling degree of individuality.

In keeping with the drawn lines of his face, and his passive attitude, Si-kahika's rather narrow torso widens in the waist, the line of the pectorals sags to form a horizontal crease, and below this the abdomen curves outward.

The cut of the large smooth wig, the sides sloping down so that the inner corners fall well below the shoulders, conforms to a fashion set earlier in the dynasty, but a later style is to be seen in the long kilt that begins above the wearer's embonpoint. Portly officials had worn long kilts ever since the Third Dynasty, if not earlier (*see* no. 5) but the upper edge never came above the navel. It is possible, of course, that the kilts were actually worn higher than they were represented; the more so since, in such cases, the long-kilted portly representation sometimes has an unusualy high navel.

During the Middle Kingdom the previous strictures concerning the location of inscriptions (as discussed in connection with no. 2) were relaxed to the point that an offering formula was permitted to appear on the front of a long kilt (*cf.* no. 16). In the present case this formula is continued on the top of the base,

in front of the feet, where the owner is identified as 'the Steward Si-kahika, true of voice, engendered by the Mistress of the House Beb . . ., true of voice'. As in the case of many of the most finished statues of the late Middle Kingdom, the hieroglyphs are clumsy and not wholly legible. If the clumsiness were confined to the line containing the names, one might suspect that this part of the inscription was added later, but the two columns containing the offering formula are executed with the same negligence.

From Karnak, late Twelfth or Thirteenth Dynasty, pink quartzite, height 65 cm.

BIBLIOGRAPHY: none.

COMMENTS: A slight vertical furrowing of the brow is noticeable in some reliefs of the Third Dynasty (nos. 4, 5) and in the statue of Ra-hotpe (Cairo Catalogue 3). In the case of Sesostris III there is either a more definite pair of vertical furrows (especially Metropolitan Museum 26.7.1394, W. C. Hayes, *Scepter of Egypt* I, p. 198, fig. 120) or a single horizontal line (*Nelson Gallery and Atkins Museum Bulletin* 4/2 [Oct. 1962], cover and p. 9). The vertical furrows recur in private statuary (Cairo *Cat. gén.* 404), and in the Eighteenth Dynasty the horizontal line may be traced on the forehead of the aged Amun-hotpe, son of Hapu (*Cat. gén.* 42127; *cf.* no. 25 below). The combination of vertical and horizontal lines is otherwise known to me in only one piece of Middle Kingdom statuary—the ivory figurine of a grimacing dwarf from Lisht (Metropolitan Museum 34.1.130, Hayes, *ibid.*, p. 223 and fig. 139). For comparable examples from the seventh century onward see Bothmer, *ESLP*, nos. 23, 68, 104, and no. 42 below. The use of yellow in representing old age is discussed in *JAOS* 2 (1963), 17–22, and some late Old Kingdom precursors of the attitude, with hands palm down upon the lap, are mentioned *ibid.*, p. 18. The name of Si-kahika does not seem to occur elsewhere. It seems to be of typical Middle Kingdom style, expressing filiation, but the element ka-hi-ka is unidentifiable, unless it is an early reference to the festival of Khoiak. The wife's name is even less intelligible. Just possibly it is related to 'long wig', *i.e.* a wig that comes down to the clavicles (*cf.* H. Ranke, *Die ägyptischen Personennamen* I, 96 [8, 9]), in which case it might be a nisba-form *Bebutet, 'Bewigged'. The accompanying facsimile is made from a rubbing kindly provided by Labib Habachi.

H.G.F.

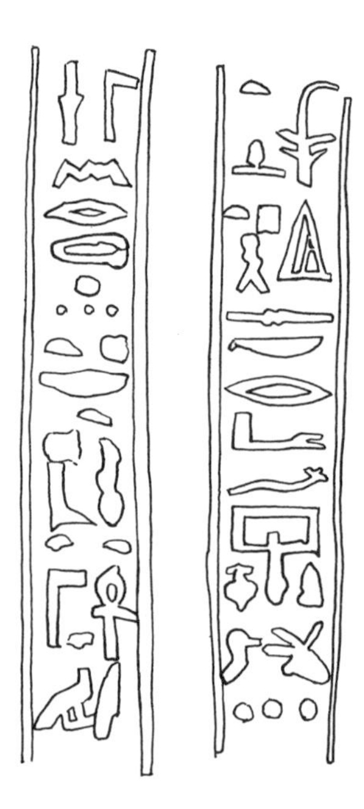

19 Broad Collar of Queen Ahhotpe

Catalogue général 52672

The wife of Seqenenre, the Theban ruler who began the expulsion of the Hyksos occupants of the Delta, and mother of King Ahmosis, who completed it, Queen Ahhotpe herself played an important part in the events of her day, and may even have acted as co-regent during the early years of Ahmosis' reign. The jewellery and weapons found in her tomb reflects contact with neighbouring lands, their crafts and customs.

Like the jewellery of Khnumet (no. 13), the magnificent collar of Ahhotpe shows Aegean influence, even though it is more essentially Egyptian in workmanship and design. This influence is seen in the flying gallop of the animals, a feature that was not entirely absent from earlier Egyptian art, but was never before so emphatically reiterated as it is here and on the blade of a knife from the queen's tomb.

The falcon-headed terminals belong to the broad collar (*wesekh*), which traditionally consisted of tubular faience beads ranged vertically in several tiers, with a series of droplike beads at the bottom. The addition of the falcon head, originally a prerogative of the king, came into funerary equipment even before the end of the Old Kingdom, but the rest of the collar remained unmodified prior to Ahhotpe's time. Living in an atmosphere of change, her craftsmen felt free to replace the staid faience beads by coursing rows of lions, ibexes and backward-glancing gazelles. Along with these are rows of appropriately sedentary cats, winged cobras and flying vultures, together with a number of abstract elements—rhomboids, disks, spirals and stylized flowers. No later collars show so lively and varied an array as this, but the same lightness survives in those belonging to the minor wives of Tuthmosis III.

The addition of wings to the uraeus cobra is known from magical devices of Middle Kingdom style, but evidently did not become a popular motif until the New Kingdom. The vulture with outspread wings is also known from earlier times, but not as a pendant, and not without some indication of the feet; this omission recalls the curious birds of Khnumet's jewellery. The use of running spirals had been almost entirely confined to scarabs in the Middle Kingdom, and their use here is doubtless to be regarded as further evidence of Aegean influence. Towards the bottom is a series of what have variously been identified as stars or crosses. The position of the loop on the back shows that they stood upright like the hieroglyph ⚘, which is generally taken to represent some sort of flower. The terminal elements resemble inverted papyrus umbels, but possibly represent blossoms of some other plant.

All of the pendants except the last are made of a single sheet of gold, with loops fixed in the concavity of the back. The pendants at the bottom have a ring for suspension and, like the falcon-headed terminals, are backed with a flat plate of gold. The terminals are attached by means of eight holes pierced through the inner edge.

A few repoussé details are added to the animals, such as the mane of the lions, but the details of the falcon heads are also enhanced with a dark pigment and the little disks have mother-of-pearl centres.

Unfortunately the original arrangement of the collar can only be deduced from the number, size and character of the elements, as well as the arrangement of the loops on the back of each piece. Von Bissing's solution to this problem is given herewith. As is noted at the end of the comments, his reconstruction includes many more elements than have been combined in recent years.

From the tomb of Ahhotpe, Thebes (Qurna), gold, width as illustrated 37.5 cm.; height of falcon heads 4.3 cm.

BIBLIOGRAPHY: W. von Bissing, *Ein thebanischer Grabfund aus dem Anfang des neuen Reichs*, p. 14 and pls. 8 (1–14), 8A, 9 (1a–f); E. Kiddle and S. Birch, *Facsimiles of the Egyptian Relics Discovered at Thebes in the Tomb of Queen Aah-hotep Exhibited in the International Exhibition of 1862*, p. 4 and pl. 11; A. Lucas, *ASAE* 27 (1927), 69–71; A. Mariette, *BIE*, prem. sér., 1 (1859), 32–6; E. Vernier, *Bijoux et orfèvreries* (*Cat. gén.*), pp. 221–2 and pl. 52; M. Vilímková, *Egyptian Jewellery*, pp. 28–9 and pl. 24.

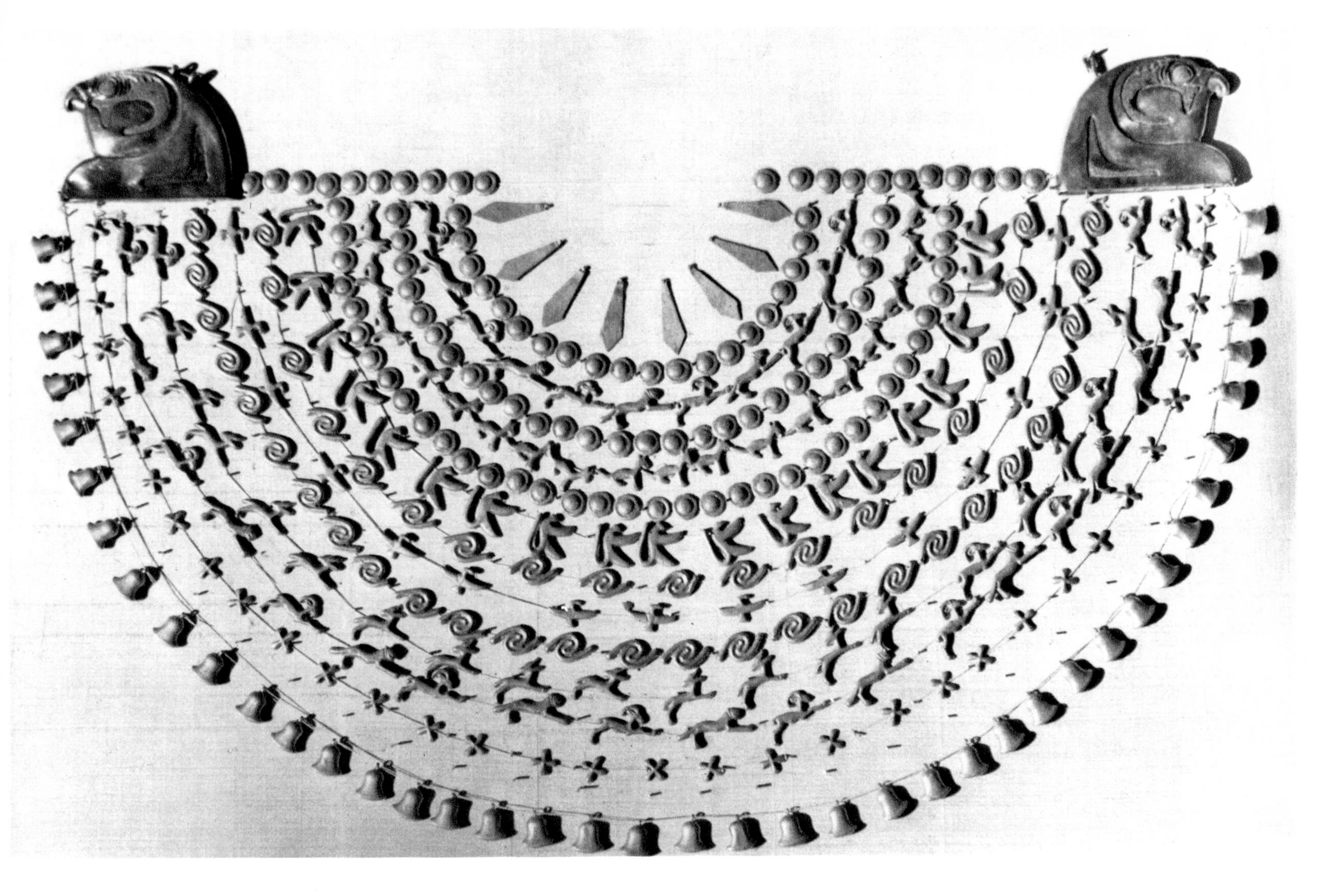

Comments: For a discussion of spirals in relation to Aegean art see Helene Kantor, *AJA* 51 (1947), 21–3, 28–30, 56–63; for the flying gallop see *ibid.*, 63–6 and W. S. Smith, *Interconnections in the Ancient Near East*, pp. 26, 155. For the broad collars dating to Tuthmosis III see H. E. Winlock, *The Treasure of Three Princesses*, pls. 10, 11 (now much more complete). A particularly close earlier parallel for the winged serpent appears on a magical knife, Louvre N 1489 (Legge, *PSBA* 27 [1905], pl. 9, fig. 15, foll. p. 152); for other serpents with outspread wings see Jéquier, *Frises d'objets*, p. 71, fig. 184 and *cf.* W. C. Hayes, *Scepter of Egypt* I, p. 249, fig. 159. Cats (both seated and recumbent) appear in amulets of earlier date (G. Brunton, *Qau and Badari* I, pl. 48 [bot. left], II, pl. 96 [26]), but the pair of seated felines represented on an Old Kingdom pectoral (Borchardt, *Statuen* I, p. 103) are evidently lions; recumbent cats are also represented on the spacers of an armlet not much earlier than the time of Queen Ahhotpe: P. Newberry and H. R. Hall, *Ancient Egyptian Art* (Burlington Fine Arts Club), p. 18 and pl. 50, B.M. 57699–57700.

The element ⚘ (Gardiner, *Grammar*, Sign List M42) rarely occurs as an independent motif before the New Kingdom (W. M. F. Petrie, *Illahun, Kahun and Gurob*, pl. 8 [58]) or during it (Petrie, *Giza and Riqqeh*, pl. 17 [26]), but very similar quatrefoils appear in Middle Kingdom ceiling patterns (W. M. F. Petrie, *Antaeopolis*, pl. 1; P. Newberry, *El Bersheh* I, p. 11) and there are more complex variations (*ibid.*, pl. 10 [35, 39]). which in turn derive from Old Kingdom floral patterns (Smith, *Art and Architecture*, fig. 21, p. 50). Patterns based on M42 turned 45 degrees also occur in the Middle Kingdom (e.g. W. M. F. Petrie, *Illahun, Kahun, Gurob*, pl. 13 [19]).

Not illustrated in this catalogue is the remainder of the elements, which are mounted separately in the Cairo Museum.

H.G.F.

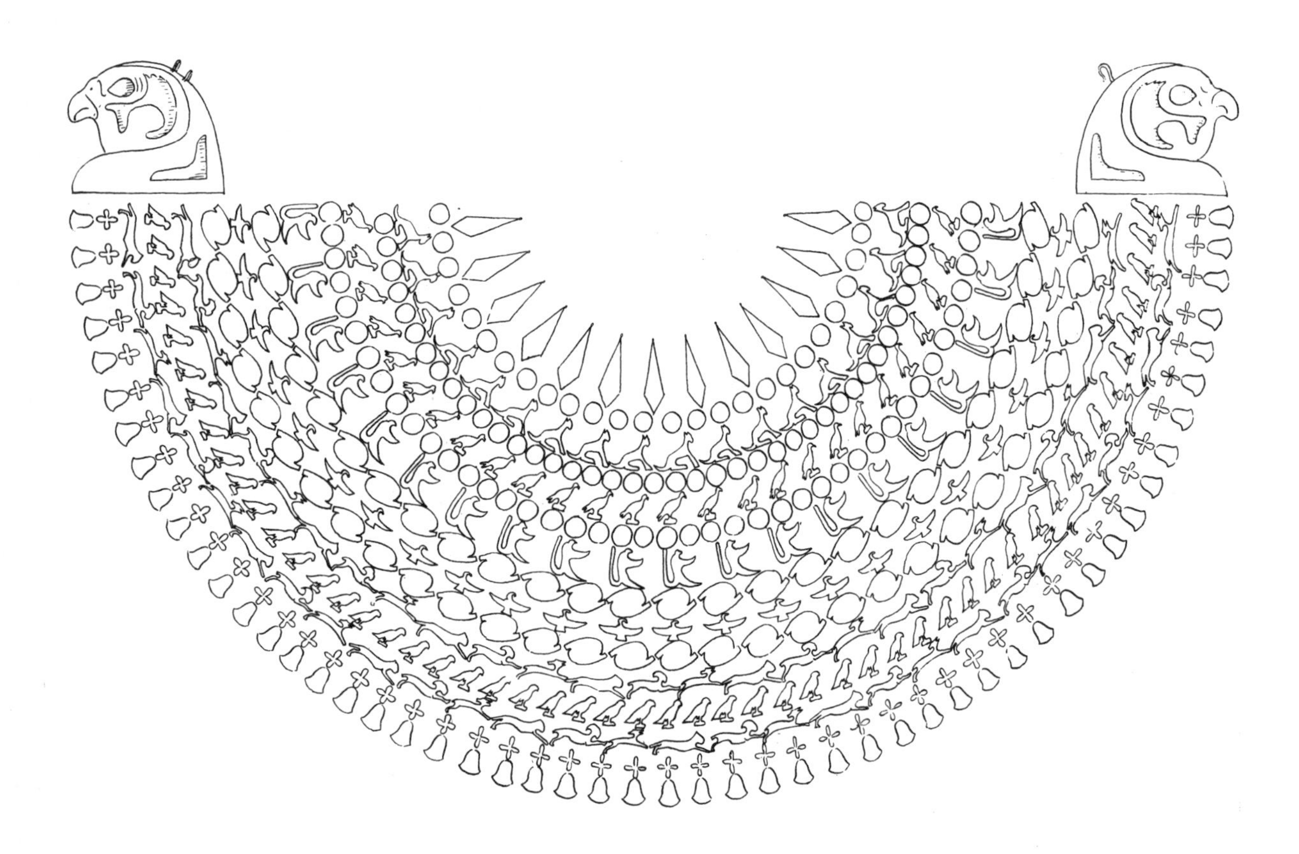

20 SENNEMUT AND THE PRINCESS NEFRU-RE

Catalogue général 42116

Although Sennemut is best known as the chief steward of Queen Hatshepsut and chief royal architect of her famous temple at Deir el Bahri (*cf.* no. 21), he began his career as the tutor and steward of her daughter Nefru-Re. This child, as the offspring of Tuthmosis II and his queen of full royal blood, should have become the queen of the king's designated successor, Tuthmosis III, whose mother was not of royal lineage. She died prematurely, however, probably before the union could be consummated, and certainly before Tuthmosis had succeeded in removing his step-mother from the throne. Sennemut was a thrifty steward, for he re-used some of the princess's bed linen for the mummy wrappings of his father Ramose whose tomb is at Thebes.

Among the several statues that represent the steward holding his young charge in a variety of attitudes, standing and seated, the present example is the most appealing. The position of the legs, while chiefly known from isolated statues of men, also lent itself to statuettes of mothers nursing their young. It occurs again in a rock-cut statue of Sennemut's brother Senmen, which similarly shows the princess, but in this case the composition is more formal and he does not hold his young charge. Here she is enveloped by Sennemut's great hands and rests securely against his upraised knee, her head further supported by a small 'back-pillar', which is a purely structural device, designed to strengthen this part of the statue. The two figures, each reduced to abstract simplification by cloaks that reveal little more than heads, hands and feet, are fitted together at right angles so that the curve of the child's sidelock neatly corresponds to the hollow of Sennemut's neck and chin. Her right hand emerges from her mantle to raise a finger to her mouth in the traditional gesture of childhood. The cobra on her brow identifies her as a princess of royal blood and the inscription beside her, on the cloak outstretched between her mentor's knees, proclaims their relationship: 'The Steward of the King's daughter Nefru-Re, Sennemut'.

The face of Sennemut is conventional and reflects none of his actual appearance as it is known from two sketches, in the Metropolitan Museum of Art, that were clearly taken from life. On the other hand, these sketches evidently portray him in his later years, whereas the statue was probably made somewhat earlier. His wig too is conventional, but it may be noted that his own hair projects from it in front of either ear, as in the case of Queen Nofret (no. 14). The corners of the eyes are prolonged by the so-called 'cosmetic-line'

that was originally confined to gods and kings, but occasionally appears on statues of private individuals in the Middle Kingdom and is much more frequent in the Eighteenth Dynasty (*cf.* no. 24).

The inscription on the base gives more of Sennemut's titles, most of them relating to the cult of the Theban god Amun; one, however, calls him 'Steward of the Mistress of the Two Lands', which is probably the equivalent of the title on his lap, for the epithet Mistress of Two Lands is applied to Nefru-Re elsewhere.

From Karnak, reign of Hatshepsut, black granite, height 60 cm.

BIBLIOGRAPHY: Legrain, *Statues* I, 64, 65 and pl. 67; C. Aldred, *New Kingdom Art in Ancient Egypt*, pl. 31; Hornemann, *Types of Ancient Egyptian Statuary*, no. 1231; Vandier, *Manuel* III, pp. 475, 505 and pl. 162 (3).

COMMENTS: For the sheets of Nefru-Re and other details about her see W. C. Hayes, *Scepter of Egypt* II, 105. The statue of Senmen is published by N. de G. Davies, *PSBA* 35 (1913), pp. 281–5 and pls. 49–53. The attitude is discussed by H. van Voss *Jaarbericht Ex Oriente Lux* 13 (1953–54), 317–21. Most of the other statues of Sennemut and Nefru-Re are shown by Aldred, *ibid.*, pls. 30–33, Vandier, *ibid.*, pl. 162 (1, 2, 5), and Hornemann, *ibid.*, nos. 1226, 1229, 1230; a list of Sennemut's statues is given by B. Switalski Lesko, *JARCE* 6 (1967), 118. For a recent discussion of his career see *ibid.*, 113–17. Still another statue of Sennemut has recently come to light, B. V. Bothner, 'Private Sculpture of Dynasty XVIII in Brooklyn', *The Brooklyn Museum Annual* 8 (1966–1967), pp. 60 ff. and figs. 5–8. Nefru-Re's titles may be found in H. Gauthier, *Le Livre des rois d'Egypte* II, 251–2.

H.G.F.

21 The Queen of Punt

12–11/26–5 (probably Journal d'Entrée 14726)

This block of relief, from Queen Hatshepsut's temple at Deir el Bahri, represents a high point in the pictorial representation of her expedition through the Red Sea to the Eritrean or Somali coast. Here the 'Great One of Punt', accompanied by his wife, greets the Egyptian royal emissary, who is out of sight. The Puntite chieftain stands before a pile of gifts and makes a gesture of reverence in the Egyptian style, for his people had been accustomed to deputations of this kind in the course of a thousand years of commerce. He is black-skinned, like the two figures behind him, has short hair, a long narrow beard, a rather Egyptian-looking white kilt and dagger, and a necklace of small round beads. Both wrists are encircled by bracelets and his entire right leg is sheathed in what appears to be a series of metal rings. The distinctive tail-like appendage at the back of the kilt may represent the end of his belt, which was probably tied at the rear as in much earlier representations of Puntites. His wife has a two-piece white dress; in addition to the usual full skirt that was generally the sole garment of women in the southern lands, she wears a sleeveless shirt. Her wavy hair is bound with a fillet and ends in a pigtail, and her necklace is an enlarged version of her husband's. Each wrist and ankle shows a pair of bracelets.

In contrast to the slenderness of the chieftain of Punt, his wife is mountainously obese. Like the queens and princesses of Karagwe, as described by John Speke, 'so large were her arms that, between the joints, the flesh hung down like large, loose-stuffed puddings'. In a lower register, where the couple appears again, he is called Pereh and she Ity; they are followed by a slender son and a fat daughter who is well on the way to emulating her mother's pendulous adiposity. In this case the chieftain's family is accompanied by 'his donkey, which carries his wife', like the noblewomen of Karagwe, she was obviously in no condition to walk. Again like the women of Karagwe, the charms of the Puntite mother and daughter were probably enlarged upon by persistent gavage. Only one non-royal woman is seen among the grass huts of the Puntite village in the Deir el Bahri reliefs, and—apart from a certain degree of steatopygia—her body and limbs are slim.

The Puntite couple reverse, to an extraordinary degree, the situation that prevailed in ancient Egypt. While Egyptian officials not infrequently display the paunchiness of their advancing years, their wives are always slender. Obviously the artist who recorded the details of Hatshepsut's expedition was fascinated by a taste in feminine pulchritude that struck him as being altogether bizarre. And at least one later artist was equally fascinated by it, as we know from a sketch of the queen that turned up at the nearby site of Deir el Medina.

An interest in the exotic was continued by Tuthmosis III, as seen by the reliefs in his portion of the Karnak temple that display the flora and fauna encountered on his military expeditions, including such peculiarities as two-tailed or three-horned cattle.

From the middle colonnade, southern wall, of the temple of Hatshepsut at Deir el Bahri, painted limestone, height 36 cm.

BIBLIOGRAPHY: A. Mariette, *Deir el Bahari*, pl. 5; E. Naville, *Temple of Deir el Bahari* III, pl. 69; W. S. Smith, *JARCE* 1 (1962), 59–61, and *Art and Architecture*, pls. 92 (B), 93 (B); S. Wenig, *Die Frau im alten Aegypten*, p. 32 and pl. 33; K. Michalowski, *The Art of Ancient Egypt*, pl. 92; P. Riesterer, *Das Ägyptische Museum Kairo*, pl. 32.

COMMENTS: For the description of the ladies of Karagwe, at the north-west corner of present-day Tanzania, see J. H. Speke, *Journal of the Discovery of the Source of the Nile* (Everyman's Library), 172, 189, 193. The later sketch, illustrated by Wenig, is in the West Berlin Museum.

In 1962 the American Research Center in Egypt presented to the Egyptian Museum a fragment discovered by Dr Nicholas Millet, which completes the back parts of the Queen's donkey shown in the register below that from which the relief exhibited here comes, see N. B. Millet, 'A Fragment of the Hatshepsut Punt Relief', *JARCE* 1 (1962), 55 ff., pls. IV, V. The fragment is restored to its original position by W. S. Smith in his reconstruction of the Puntite scene, *JARCE* 1 (1962), fig. on p. 61.

H.G.F.

22 Statue of Tuthmosis III

Catalogue général 42054

Less than five feet four inches in height 'this Napoleonic little man,' as William C. Hayes says, 'was incontestably the greatest pharaoh ever to occupy the throne of Egypt.' The statue of him that is shown here is only two-thirds life size, but it bespeaks his energetic character, the sureness of his administration, and the irresistible success of his conquests. While the same standard of classical perfection survived into the following reign the reign of Tuthmosis III marked the zenith of New Kingdom adherence to tradition, at the same time that his consolidation of the Egyptian empire paved the way for further changes.

In the finish of its greywacke surface, and the remarkable plasticity of its face, this statue technically surpasses even the best Fourth Dynasty work in softer materials such as limestone, although its very perfection somewhat deprives it of the vitality of older masterpieces. Rather more idealized than its well-known companion piece in the Cairo Museum of the same material and twice the scale, it nonetheless conveys the essential features of the king's appearance: a shallowness of the eye-sockets, which contributes to the blandness of his expression, a prominent aquiline nose, straight upper lip and broad chin.

Save in minor details, the headcloth and uraeus, ceremonial beard and pleated kilt conform to ancient tradition, as does the cloth object called a *nemes* that is held in the right hand. The throne name (prenomen) of Tuthmosis appears on his kilt: Men-kheper-Re, 'The Form of Re Abides'. The backpillar presents a fuller version of the royal protocol, beginning with the falcon of Horus, with whom every king was identified (*cf.* no. 6).

See also Colour Plate VI.

From Karnak, reign of Tuthmosis III, dark greywacke, height 90 cm.

Bibliography: Legrain, *Statues* I, 32–3; Vandier, *Manuel* I, pp. 202–3, 205 and pl. 100 (1); B. Hornemann, *Types of Ancient Egyptian Statuary*, n. 143; *Tel*, pl. 80; W. Westendorf, *Ancient Egypt*, p. 105; Lange and Hirmer, *Egypt*, pls. 142, 143. Kodansha, pl. 64 (colour).

Comments: The quotation is from Chapter IX, section 2, of the revised *Cambridge Ancient History*.

H.G.F.

23 Amenophis II

Catalogue général 42077

The king stands in the classical attitude, left foot forward, hands held to the sides clutching the emblematic staves. He wears a rather rare form of headcloth called the *khat*, a kind of hood which holds the hair loosely in a bag. The uraeus rises from the lower edge of the headband, while the coils are placed high on the crown of the headcloth. The king is clothed in a belted *shendyt* kilt with his name inscribed on the belt. The relief brows are heavy, squared off at the outer ends but rounded where they join the root of the nose prominently. While flat over the tops of the eyes, the brows follow the outlines of the eyes as they curve down to the outer corners. The upper lid is in sharp relief and is continued in a cosmetic line which widens toward a squared end whilst the lower lid is plastic. The mouth is wide and flat with sharp outlines, the ears large and thick, and the chin, which is small in profile, is square and broad in front. The square face is emphasized by the angular structure of the nose and brows. This compact, tight construction of the sculpture continues throughout the rest of the body, in the heavy shoulders, muscular legs, and especially in the small, only slightly modelled torso.

The sculpture signals the end of the idealism established during the first part of the Eighteenth Dynasty, and which is especially well-represented in the statues of Sennemut and Tuthmosis III (nos. 20 and 22). With his serious, open-eyed face, Amenophis II conveys the majesty and dignity of the great rulers who founded the Eighteenth Dynasty and built Egypt into a world power. Amenophis II prided himself as a great sportsman, a hint of which is contained in the strong muscles of his sculptures. On the other hand, the smooth, even voluptuous treatment of the headcloth of this statue suggests the svelte elegance of the later half of the Dynasty. The spherical mass of the headcloth is emphatically repeated in the rounded muscle of the shoulder, but more discretely in the breast.

See also Colour Plate V.

From the Karnak cachette, Eighteenth Dynasty, greywacke (right leg restored below knee, left foot missing, repair over left knee), height 57 cm.

Bibliography: *5000 Years Catalogue*, London, no. 55; Vandier, *Manuel* III, pp. 306–7, pl. 101, 2; Aldred, *New Kingdom Art in Ancient Egypt*, pl. 51.

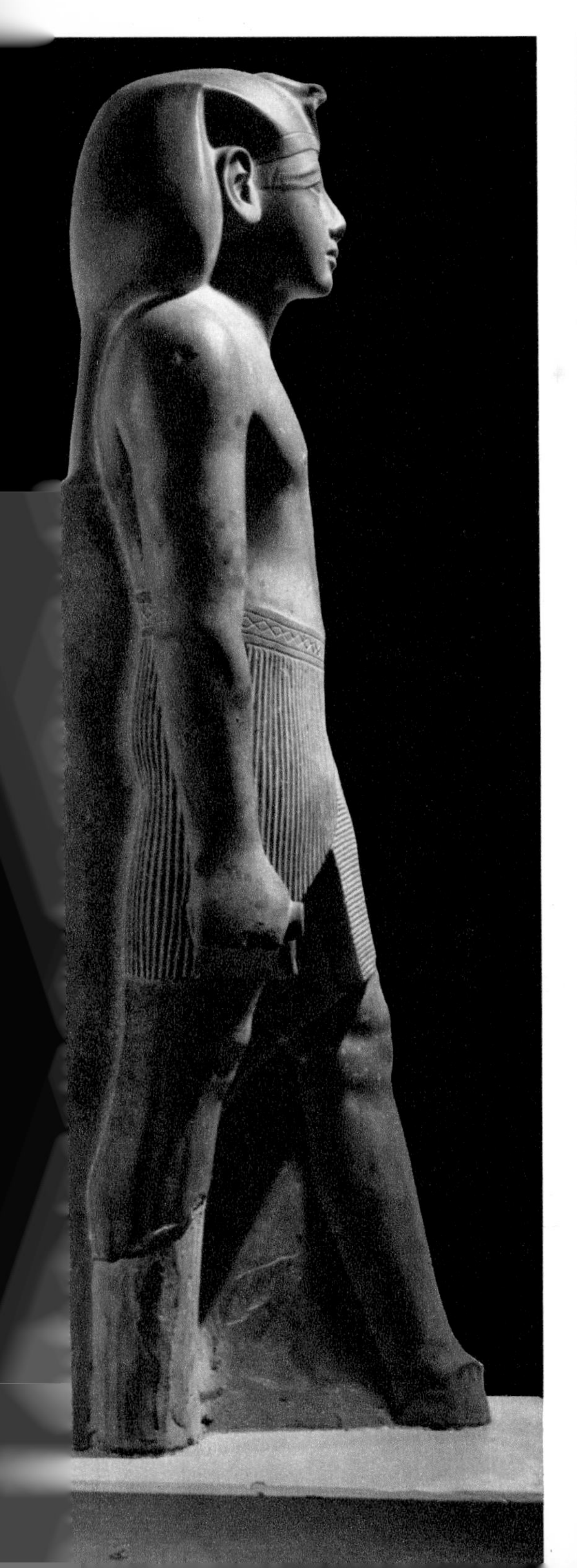

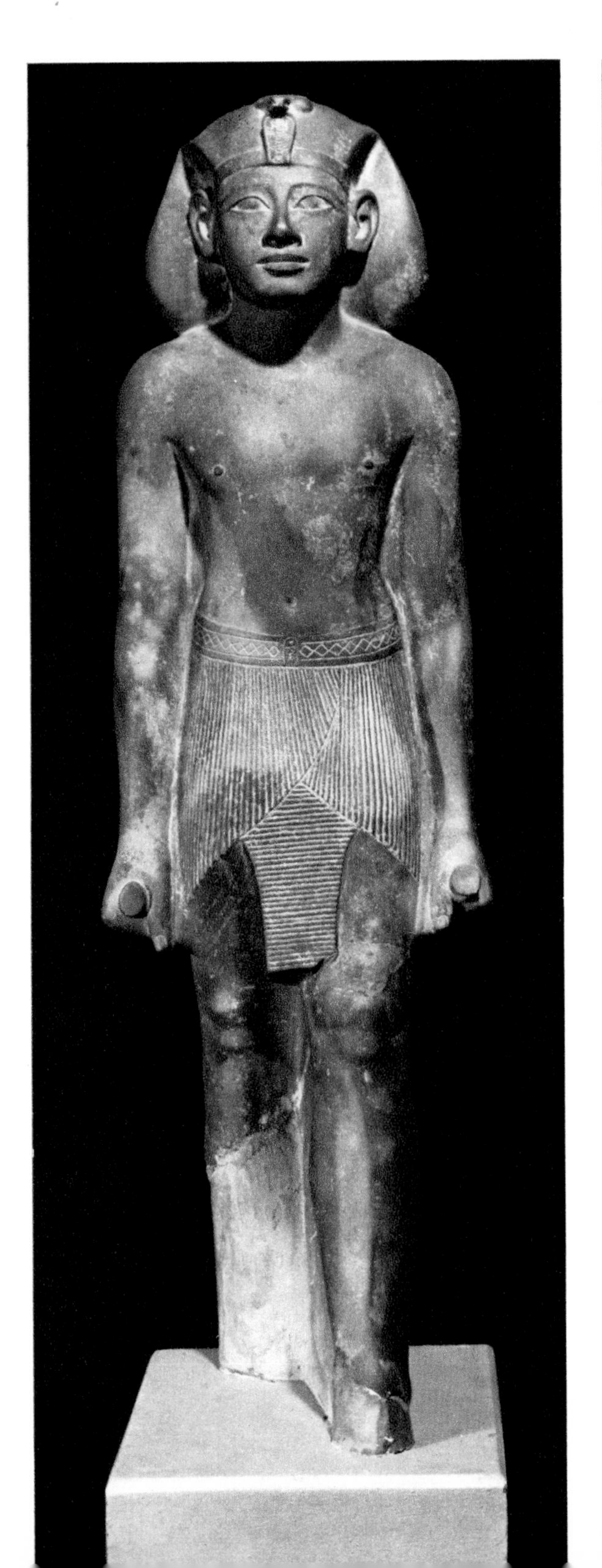

COMMENTS: Bothmer, *BMFA* 52 (1954) 11 ff., and Vandier, *op. cit.*, pp. 305 ff., have divided the many preserved sculptures of Amenophis II into two categories, one showing the king early in his reign, and the other representing him as an older man. While the two categories certainly exist, it is with some difficulty that one accepts the hypothesis of a 'younger' and an 'older' portrait. Bothmer is correct in defining the second category as a more idealizing type, and places our statue here. But the facial type does not seem to portray a man any older than, let us say, *Cat. gén.* 42073, which belongs to the first category and therefore, according to Bothmer, Vandier, and Aldred (*cf.* pl. 52 of *New Kingdom Art*) earlier than our no. 23. Possibly the answer to the problem lies in the existence of two main workshops at Thebes, one working in a more idealizing tradition, the other somewhat more inventive in its treatment of the face. Nevertheless, Amenophis II was king for more than twenty-five years and we might expect the adventurous artists of this flourishing age to develop a new stylistic iconography during such a long reign.

There are sculptures of Amenophis II in both Boston and New York. A small head of white crystalline limestone in Boston joins a body inscribed by Amenophis II in the Louvre (Bothmer, *op. cit.*). Vandier has made the objection, *Manuel* III, p. 306, that the mouth of the Boston head is smiling, which is untypical of all other sculptures of Amenophis II. This, with other features much closer to the type of Tuthmosis III, brings Vandier to the conclusion that the Boston–Louvre statuette belonged to Tuthmosis III and was usurped by Amenophis II (at least one usurpation did occur: the belt of the Louvre body is inscribed by Tuthmosis IV; the name of Amenophis occurs on the front of the base). The Boston face, however, seems rather too delicate for Tuthmosis III. The statuette represents the king kneeling in presentation of unguent jars, a type which is common in reliefs showing the coronation ceremony. Perhaps the sculpture was made at the very beginning of Amenophis II's reign, when the sculptors were still influenced by the type of Tuthmosis III. Another head in Boston (Bothmer, *op. cit.*, 29.1132) comes from Semna in the Sudan and belongs in the second or 'late' category, but is distinctly provincial in workmanship. A fine limestone statuette of the same king is in New York and belongs to the second category (Bothmer, *ibid.*, 13.182.6). In nearly all the sculptures of Amenophis II the uraeus begins from the lower edge of the headband of the crown. MMA 44.4.68, a bust assigned by Aldred to Amenophis II (*New Kingdom Art*, pl. 64) has a uraeus which springs from the upper edge of the band, as does a head in Baltimore, 22.229, another sculpture thought by Aldred (pl. 65) to represent Amenophis II.

For the *khat* wig see Vandier, *Manuel* III, p. 310. From the back descends an unusually wide flap which is not the usual braid found, for instance, on the *nemes*. As throughout this sculpture, the edges are rounded, adding to the feeling of smoothness which pervades the work.

E.L.B.T.

24 Sen-nufer and his Wife

Catalogue général 42126

Seated side by side, their arms interlaced in the fashion of the New Kingdom, the Mayor of the Southern City (Thebes) and his wife Senay are presented against a backing from which their bodies only partially emerge. This feature, in keeping with the rather flat treatment of the extended arms and hands, conforms to the function of the group as a monument that called for the attention of visitors to the temple of Karnak, where it was placed. It is evident that such attention was frequently received, for the upper part of the inscriptions, on the lap of each figure, has been erased by the ministrations of those who invoked 'everything goodly and pure' for the spirits of the deceased couple, in some cases supplementing their words with actual offerings and libations.

In common with several other Eighteenth Dynasty groups, a child appears in the space between the legs of the two seated figures—a daughter named Mut-nofret. This space is filled to a higher level than the seat itself and the top of the daughter's head rises slightly above it, just as the crowns of her parents clear the backing behind them. The right side of the seat shows an incised figure of the same daughter, who is seated with her legs folded under her, while the left side bears an identical representation of her sister Nefertiry. They are accompanied by offerings as well as an offering formula in which they are mentioned along with their father. The back is inscribed with longer inscriptions of the same kind in favour of him and also for his wife.

Sen-nufer is represented as a man of sedentary affluence, his abdomen creased with rolls of fat in a style that is set by some Middle Kingdom bureaucrats long before his time. His left shoulder is blazoned with royal cartouches, each surmounted by ostrich plumes and rams horns and supported by a winged disk, and containing the distinctive 'throne name' of Amenophis II. Such cartouches make their first appearance on private statues dating to the preceding reign of Tuthmosis III, and become more frequent and conspicuous during the later New Kingdom. They represent a further departure from the Old Kingdom stricture against the inappropriate application of inscriptions to the statue proper (*cf.* nos. 2, 16). The shoulder-length wig is characteristic of the reign of Amenophis II, showing the beginning of a distinction between the striated surface and the underside, as revealed by a triangular series of overlapping locks on either side of the face. Four massive necklaces, consisting of disklike elements, represent the current form of

the 'gold of favour' that was bestowed by the king, which again appears for the first time in the reign of Tuthmosis III, along with the heavy armlets that often accompany it.

Beneath the necklace is a pair of heart-shaped amulets such as Sen-nufer also wears in his painted tomb, famous for its vine-covered ceiling. In some cases the paintings show the hearts inscribed with the name of Amenophis II, but in one case the name is Alexander—carefully painted in hieroglyphs by a tourist who visited the tomb a thousand years after Sen-nufer's death (*right*).

Senay's costume is altogether conventional; her single bracelet, broad collar and long dress are known from the Old Kingdom, while her wig continues the evolution of the tripartite wig in a form that is common in the early Eighteenth Dynasty. This has something in common with the massive 'Hathorian' wig of the Twelfth Dynasty, but the tresses on either side of the face fall straight downward covering the ears; the

resemblance is more apparent from the side, where the division between the three main components is seen to begin at a relatively high point, isolating the locks at the rear. The wig of the daughter is more remarkable, with one series of vertical twisted ends emerging from beneath another as they spread out to cover her shoulders.

Sen-nufer's features are heavier than those of his wife, and his eyebrows turn down more sharply at the sides to meet the 'cosmetic line' that prolongs the corner of the eye; in this respect he resembles his ruler (no. 23). As in the case of his wife, however, the corners of the mouth are slightly contracted so that each wears a very faint smile recalling that of Queen Nofret (no. 14).

The statue is among the few works of Egyptian art that are 'signed'. A supplementary four-column inscription on the left side tells that it was made by two artists ('outline scribes') of the temple of Amun—Amenmose and Djed-Khons.

From Karnak, reign of Amenophis II, black granite, height 120 cm.

Bibliography: Legrain, *Statues* I, pp. 76–8 and pl. 75; Bodil Hornemann, *Types of Ancient Egyptian Statuary*, nos. 1420–1421; C. Aldred, *New Kingdom Art in Ancient Egypt*, p. 61 and pl. 62; Vandier, *Manuel* III, pp. 511–12 and pl. 147 (1). On the subject of artists' signatures see Edith Ware, *AJSL* 43 (1927), 185–207 and Smith, *HESPOK*, 356.

Comments: The bottom of the cartouches is not in the form of a bow (⊂⊃), as Legrain states; the winged disk resembles the tie that usually appears at this point, and is clearly inspired by that detail. The position of the interlaced arms is discussed by Spiegelberg, *JEA* 15 (1929), 199, and the 'gold of favour' by Schäfer, *ÄZ* 70 (1934), 10–13. For the tomb of Sen-nufer see *PM* I, Pt. 1, 197–203; a particularly good view in colour, including the detail shown here, is given in J. Yoyotte, *Treasures of the Pharaohs*, p. 79. The titles are listed by H. W. Helck, *Zur Verwaltung des Mittleren und Neuen Reichs*, 525–6.

H.G.F.

25 Scribal Statue of Amen-hotpe, Son of Hapu

Journal d'Entrée 44861

Emblazoned, like Sen-nufer, with the cartouches of the king whom he served, the inscription on his lap similarly effaced by the pious ministrations of visitors to the temple of Karnak, where it was placed, this superb statue represents the renowned director of works of Amenophis III. So great was his esteem that he was accorded a funerary temple in western Thebes among the royal temples, and comparable to them in grandeur. At the end of the Eighteenth Dynasty the statue was removed, together with an almost identical companion piece, to a place of honour at the gateway of the tenth pylon of the Karnak Temple, where it was accompanied by similar statues of Pa-Ra-messu, later Ramesses I.

Amen-hotpe sits crosslegged in the classic attitude of scribes, an emblematic palette slung over his left shoulder, and an actual palette, in the form of a clam shell, on his left knee. Both palettes show a pair of disks representing cakes of red and black ink. His left hand unrolls the papyrus that is spread out upon his lap, and the other is poised to write, although the worn inscription beneath it is already complete and, as usual, is in monumental hieroglyphic script rather than the cursive hieratic that was normally employed for hieratic records. His flaccid torso shows the same creases that appear on Sen-nufer's statue, but it is rendered with greater realism and finish. The head, meditatively inclined over his work, wears a wig that is a more developed version of the one worn by Sen-nufer; the undercut portion is more clearly defined and the edge passes over the tops of the ears to form a more continuous curve. Amen-hotpe's face has something of the almond-eyed look of his royal master, but the high arch of his brows is distinctive and, from a comparison with another statue of the same man in the Cairo Museum, made when he was eighty years old (page 118) it is evident that both statues capture much of his actual appearance—specifically the rather long face, the straight line of the mouth, and the square chin.

In accordance with the rather literal-minded logic of the Egyptians, the inscription on the papyrus is turned towards the scribe, so that one must read over his shoulder. Among other things, it records the fact that Amen-hotpe made large statues of the king which were placed on the west—presumably west of Thebes. As Legrain pointed out long ago, these were probably the colossi of Memnon, which stood before the now-vanished mortuary temple of Amenophis III. The base of the statue bears an equally interesting inscription. After repeating the titles and names of the owner, it says: 'O ye Upper and Lower Egyptians,

and every eye that beholds the sun disk, who come downstream and upstream to Thebes to supplicate to the Lord of Gods: Come unto me, and I will report to Amun of Opet what ye have to say. And make the offering ritual and libations for me with what is with you. For I, by the king's grace, am an intercessor who will give the suppliant a hearing and will advance the affairs of the Two Lands.'

While part of this inscription was concealed when the statue was moved to its place of honour, no one had to read it to be aware of the intercessor's virtues, and to give him his due of veneration. By that time he was already well on the way to canonization and his reputation increased steadily thereafter until, in the Ptolemaic Period, he was actually worshipped among the gods.

From the tenth pylon of the temple of Karnak, reign of Amenophis III, black granite, height 128 cm.

BIBLIOGRAPHY: G. Legrain, *ASAE* 14 (1914), 13–26; Vandier, *Manuel* III, 515 and pl. 171 (3); C. Aldred, *New Kingdom Art in Ancient Egypt*, pl. 91; Lange and Hirmer, *Egypt*, pl. 158; *Toutankhamon et son temps*, no. 2.

COMMENTS: For the identical statue (*J. d'E.* 44862) see Legrain, *ibid.*, and Hornemann, *Types of Ancient Egyptian Statuary*, no. 431; for the older representation see Vandier, *ibid.*, pl. 149 (5), Aldred, *ibid.*, pl. 92; Lange and Hirmer, *ibid.*, pl. 159; a more conventional representation of Amen-hotpe (*Cat. gén.* 551) is shown by Vandier, *ibid.*, pl. 171 (4). Further information concerning Amen-hotpe may be found in Sethe's article in *Festschrift Ebers*, pp. 110–16; also A. Varille and C. Robichon, *Le temple du scribe royal Amenhotep fils de Hapou*, H. Wild, *MDIK* 16 (1958), 406–13; M. Malinine, *Rev. d'Eg.* 14 (1962), 37–43.

H.G.F.

26 Colossal head of Akhenaten

29–5/49–1

This extraordinary head and its companions are unique in the entire history of Egyptian art. At the beginning of his reign, when he still called himself Amenophis IV, Akhenaten began the construction of a huge temple to the Aten east of the Karnak temple. The decoration of this temple, consisting of many thousands of uniformly-sized blocks of relief, illustrate how severely Akhenaten led his artists to break with tradition and to experiment with what is the only genuinely new style during the many millennia of Egyptian art. This first style of the Amarna Period indulges in peculiarly expressionistic forms and lines which may be called grotesque when compared with what came before and after. These reliefs have been uncovered in the foundations of buildings constructed by later kings. The foundations of the Aten Temple itself have been only partially explored. What was apparently the forecourt of the temple revealed a number of statues, each about thirteen feet high, which stood against huge pillars lining the court. Only the foundations of the pillars have been preserved. The statues imitate in form much earlier figures representing the king as the resurrected Osiris, dressed in mummy-wrappings which completely covered the body from the neck down. The earlier representations show the arms crossed, as they are here, clutching the crook and flail. Akhenaten, however, chose to install a new type altogether: the king is no longer the resurrected deity, but the living image of himself as the Aten, for he wears the normal attire of the ruling king, an aproned kilt. One very astonishing version appears to show the king naked and sexless. This has led to much speculation concerning the physiology of the heretic of Amarna. Furthermore, the sculptures show the king with enormously widened hips, pendulous abdomen and heavy breasts. The heads, like the one exhibited here, are grotesquely distorted: the face is long and narrow, the chin and cheek bones angular and elongated, the eyes narrow, overlong, and hooded, the lips huge, pendulous, sensual. The thin fold of flesh between nostrils and lips is emphasized by the pouched flesh at the corners of the mouth. These remarkable innovations have been described by Aldred as having '. . . been exaggerated to such an extent as to lose their natural significance and to take on a new super-human symbolism—a stigmata.'

The expressionism of these sculptures is unique and even in the sculpture in relief of the earlier Amarna Period never reaches such a totally overpowering effect (*cf.* no. 28). The humanism of the living god as represented in the statue of Chephren (no. 6) or the classic idealism of Tuthmosis III and Amenophis II

(nos. 22, 23) have been replaced by something which is more fearful, more private, less comprehensible to any but a purely emotional response. The boldness of the sculpture was not possible without a complete revolution in ideology and this must be attributed solely to the almost egotistical passion of Akhenaten himself. However, he had at his disposal workmen at Thebes who were already experimenting with new forms under his father Amenophis III (*cf.* no. 25). These artists were able to create new concepts under the influence of the ideological fervour of the revolution.

Each of the figures wears a different crown; the head here wears a *nemes* headcloth surmounted by what appears to be the lower part of the Red Crown. The right arm is adorned with huge bezels of a bracelet, bearing the early names of the Aten.

From Karnak, Aten Temple, Eighteenth Dynasty, painted sandstone (most colours gone), height 153 cm.

BIBLIOGRAPHY: *Toutankhamon et son temps*, no. 3, with earlier bibliography; C. Aldred, *Akhenaten*, pl. 4.

COMMENTS: See Aldred, *New Kingdom Art in Ancient Egypt*, nos. 107–9 for companion pieces, and pp. 22 ff. for comments about the early part of the Amarna period. See especially Aldred, *Akhenaten*, for a full

and detailed study of the period. In chapter VIII, 'The Pathology of Akhenaten', there is a full discussion of the most recent studies of the physiological problems which helped to lead to the new style in art. The wrinkles of the throat and the pierced ears are innovations immediately preceding Akhenaten's reign and later become standard features of Ramesside sculpture. The earlier mummiform Osirid statues (*e.g.* of Amenophis I) bear the names of the king himself rather than that of a deity. An interesting confirmation of the continuation of Amenophis III's school of sculptors into the reign of Akhenaten is provided by the recently re-discovered stela of Bak, Chief Sculptor and Master of Works of Akhenaten. Bak's father was a Chief Sculptor under Amenophis III. This stela appears to refer to the earlier version of the Aten's name and shows Bak (carved in the round except for the back, which is attached to the stela) with some distortions, although not yet extreme, of the early Amarna period; see Aldred, *Akhenaten*, pl. 79. *Ibid.*, pl. 4, illustrating our head, suggests that these sculptures were perhaps designed by Bak himself. This is not the place to discuss the vexed problem of the existence, or lack, of a co-regency between Akhenaten and his father Amenophis III, although the implications for the development of the art of Amarna are vital. Smith, *Art and Architecture*, chapters 14 and 16, are helpful in surveying some of the problems. More specialized studies have contributed little to the art-historical questions.

E.L.B.T

27 Drawing of a Princess

Journal d'Entrée 48035

This sketch is one of the loveliest drawings preserved from ancient Egypt. Yet the drawing was not meant to be preserved: it is a sculptor's trial piece and already the artist has begun to carve the lower part of the figure. It is likely, although not certain, that one of the princesses of the Royal Family of Amarna is represented. She sinks into a soft cushion and bites into a duckling held in her right hand, while reaching for a bunch of grapes with her left hand. On the table are onions, figs and variously shaped cakes; a wine-jug stands nearby. The little princess wears a gown of transparent linen which is indicated by a few deft lines. The folds of her neck are drawn in profile, with the addition of the lines characteristic of the period. A lock of hair hangs over the elongated cranium (*cf.* no. 28, standing princess). The downturned full lips, extended chin, high eyebrow, and profile of forehead and nose are features of the developed Amarna style, as is the prominent abdomen with the fold which is frequently found in seated figures during the period. Both feet are shown pulled up on the front side of the cushion and the toes are realistically placed, the large toe of the left foot being enlarged somewhat to indicate its presence behind the right foot. A slight attempt has been made in relief to illustrate the bent kneecap.

It is clear that the artist has tried in both drawing and relief to manipulate light, to accentuate more important elements and even to indicate to some extent a single origin of light. Thus the already carved areas are cut more deeply on the left side of the stone than on the right. In the drawing, there is a tendency to use heavier lines above than below and on the left, although this usage is inconsistent.

The delicacy of the workmanship suggests that this precious little fragment of the artist's personal thoughts was made in the later Amarna period, when the experiments of the earlier period were rationalized into a more restrained style, reflecting movements which had begun already at the end of the reign of Amenophis III. The flowing lines are in marked contrast to the attenuated, gaunt forms of nos. 26 and 28.

From Amarna, North Palace, limestone, with drawing lines in black pigment, late Eighteenth Dynasty, height 23.5 cm.

Bibliography: *Toutankhamon et son temps*, no. 8, with earlier bibliography.

COMMENTS: The intimacy of the royal family engaged in private activities is characteristic and unique to the Amarna period. The relaxed position and depressed pillow are also typical, *cf.* no. 28; and especially the famous painting from Amarna which shows two princesses seated on cushions by the side of their mother (Ashmolean Museum, Oxford; Davies, *Ancient Egyptian Paintings*, pl. LXXIV; colour reproduction from original in Yoyotte, *Treasures of the Pharaohs*, p. 107). The restrained, later Amarna style is especially evident in the reliefs transported from Amarna to Hermopolis across the Nile by Ramesses II and used by him as foundation blocks, see J. Cooney, *Amarna Reliefs from Hermopolis in American Collections*. The sketch exhibited here was possibly made midway between the early and late styles. The curving lines and soft forms of the end of the reign of Amenophis III are especially evident in the tombs of Ramose and Kheruef at Thebes, both of which contain work of the periods of Akhenaten and his father, *cf.* Lange and Hirmer, *Egypt*, pls. 166–78.

E.L.B.T.

28 Stela with the Royal Family

Journal d'Entrée 44865

The stela shows Akhenaten, Nefertiti and their eldest daughters: Meryt-Aten, Maket-Aten, and Ankh-es-en-pa-Aten (later the wife of Tut-ankh-Amun with the name Ankh-es-en-Amun). Above the family is the sun-disk Aten, with its characteristic rays ending in hands pouring out its creative forces to the Royal Family. The disk itself lies under the hieroglyphic sign for sky, which extends across the width of the stela. Both king and queen receive the breath of life from the disk: held to their nostrils by the rays are the signs of life, *ankh*. All the figures are relaxed in a scene of a purely private nature: Akhenaten is

presenting his daughters with jewels, and the eldest, Meryt-Aten, receives an earring directly from her father, to join the one she already wears. The jewel consists of a disk, probably of gold, with beads strung below. A second earring lies on Akhenaten's knees beside two collars of beads. Meanwhile, Maket-Aten, standing on her mother's knees and touching her chin in an intimate gesture, holds out another earring which her sister Ankh-es-en-pa-Aten fondles. The latter's head is supported by her mother's left hand. Nefertiti reaches out with her right hand to pat the head of Meryt-Aten. The three little daughters are nude and Meryt-Aten appears to show the developments of early adolescence. The king wears a pleated garment which falls over his knees and the so-called blue- or war-crown, which this peaceful monarch affected frequently. Nefertiti wears a long gown which is tied high under her breasts. The long ribbons hang loosely over her knees and hips. She wears the crown which is unique to her; shaped like the Red Crown of Lower Egypt without the vertical element rising at the back. Streamers hang down her back and over her shoulder. Both parents wear sandles and heavy collars. They are seated on cushioned chairs, the sides of which are sketchily decorated with the joined plants of Upper and Lower Egypt (*cf.* no. 6). Footrests support the royal feet. The entire scene rests on a platform of bound rushes, perhaps indicating a rush mat.

The style is severe and highly mannered: a work of earlier Amarna. The chins and crania are highly exaggerated, necks are thin and thrust forward, the arms and legs spindly. The abdominal muscles are flabby and pendulous and the forms loose despite the taut line enclosing them.

The stela and its decoration are a contradiction in terms. On the one hand, the subject is one which should take place in the royal harem: the scene is entirely intimate. Yet the stela was set up as a household shrine in a private house where it was presumably the focal point of private worship of the Royal Family as the incarnate Aten, the children perhaps particularly representing the creative powers of the Aten. On the other hand, the super-human imagery (*cf.* no. 26) imposed on the family group gives the force needed in the stela's function as a religious monument. Thus the paradox of apparently soft forms mingled with grotesque is resolved and we may even find these earlier monuments more successful than the later, sinuous style.

From Amarna, limestone with traces of colour, late Eighteenth Dynasty, height 44 cm.

Bibliography: *Toutankhamoun et son temps*, no. 4, with earlier bibliography.

Comments: The names of the Aten are those instituted in Year 8 of Akhenaten's reign (see *Toutankhamoun et son temps* for references). A stela of similar composition, with slightly different subject-matter (the king holds one of his daughters in his arms, kissing her), is in Berlin, Lange and Hirmer, *Egypt*, pl. 184. Its style is even closer to the extremism of the early period, and it too seems to have been used as a private shrine. In both cases there is an astonishing formal and psychological relationship which creates compositional unity. Traces of blue fill the inscriptions and elsewhere, and traces of red are found on both gowns. The crowns are blue, now oxidized. A film of brown iron oxide covers much of the stela, a deposit formed *in situ*. The rectangular stela is topped by a cavetto cornice. On the front of the base are emplacements for door posts. The doors are shown in a reconstruction made by the German excavators and reproduced in *Toutankhamoun et son temps*, p. 41. The inscription gives the names of the Royal Family and the Aten. The poignancy of the family group becomes an anomaly if one considers the points made by Aldred, *Akhenaten*, chapter VIII, concerning the hypothetical sexual inadequacy of Akhenaten.

E.L.B.T.

29 A Scribe and the God of Writing

Journal d'Entrée 59291

A scribe is seated with his legs tucked under him, in the manner of Amen-hotpe, Son of Hapu (no. 25). On his knees he holds a scroll of papyrus, the roll of which he holds in his left hand. On his left knee is a palette. His right hand is clutched as if holding a pen. Above the scribe, on a cavetto-corniced stand or altar, squats a baboon crowned with the horned sun-disk: it is the image of Thoth, god of writing and patron of scribes. Of all the bureaucratic professions of ancient Egypt, none was more honoured than that of the scribe, and Thoth himself was scribe of the gods and therefore privy to their secrets. Thereby he held great power; in another aspect Thoth was the heart of Ra—the heart was the seat of intelligence, and writing was the physical manifestation of intelligence. The baboon is also the greeter of the sun and is shown as such in reliefs from the Aten Temple at Karnak.

The head of the scribe slouches forward, whereas Amen-hotpe's bends forward deliberately. A pendulous paunch and soft, prominent breasts complete this picture of a physique gone to seed during years of work in the scriptorium. Yet, in striking contrast, the face has that gaunt, haunted appearance characteristic of the Amarna artists. The long nose and pointed chin are matched by sharp cheek bones and overlong, narrow eyes. The double wig is cut low over the forehead and hangs heavily over the neck and shoulders. Striated curls run over the horizontally waved outer wig. The scribe wears a short-sleeved high-necked garment which reaches to his knees. His ears are notched in the late Eighteenth Dynasty manner.

The baboon of Thoth is heavily maned. The thick fur hanging over the upper part of his body is leaf-patterned in the curious way often found in ancient Near Eastern art. A small, but prominent rump and tiny legs support the heavy weight of the torso. As usual in representations of the baboon, the penis is prominent but not ithyphallic (*cf.* no. 35).

No inscription tells us who the scribe is. He and his works remain anonymous. The charming, intimate, evocative sculpture was found in the residential quarter of Amarna, and we must assume that it was placed as a votive in one of those private shrines which are represented by the stela no. 28. Extremely few private sculptures from Amarna are preserved. This one, perhaps more than any other, gives us some insight into the style of private art; and even more eloquently, it provides a clearer idea than any other of how the resident of Amarna wished himself to be remembered.

As always in ancient Egyptian art, the quality of monumentality is successfully imparted to even the smallest sculpture.

From Amarna, late Eighteenth Dynasty, probably serpentine, set into limestone base, height of sculpture 14 cm., length of base 11.2 cm.

BIBLIOGRAPHY: Pendlebury, *JEA* 19 (1933), pls. XVII–XVIII, 1–2; Vandier, *Manuel* III, pp. 450, 518, pl. 171, 5; Aldred, *New Kingdom Art in Ancient Egypt*, pl. 143.

COMMENTS: Remarkably enough, the statuette is not exceptional in type and several others like it have been preserved. The Louvre (E 11153 and 11154, Vandier, *op. cit.*, pl. 150, 1, 2) possesses two of precisely the same type; however, the scribes face to the left of the baboon instead of the right. East Berlin possesses still a third which, like ours, is set into a base (wood): Staatliche Museen zu Berlin, *Führer durch des Berliner Ägyptisches Museum* (1961), fig. 22; also Bothmer, *BMFA* 47 (1949) 46, fig. 7 (Berlin Inv. No. 20001).

In West Berlin is the tiny figure of a scribe which must have come from a similar group. This last figure was also excavated at Amarna (Staatliche Museen Preussischer Kulturbesitz, *Ägyptisches Museum Berlin* [1967] no. 553). Bothmer and Vandier (*op. cit.*) wish to place all these figures before the Amarna period, and Vandier, *op. cit.*, p. 518, suggests that our no. 29 was taken to Amarna after it had been made during the reign of Amenophis III. The face of our sculpture is enough to show that it was made during the Amarna period, not before. The eyebrows of the figures in the Louvre and West Berlin have that bent angle over the outer corner of the eye which is standard in the reign of Amenophis III (*cf.* no. 25). The Berlin brows are in relief; the Louvre brows only slightly. The West Berlin statuette has the double folds under the breast which are a feature of Eighteenth Dynasty sculpture but which rarely appear in the Amarna period, when the folds are usually smoothed out into the period's characteristic hanging breasts and belly. A problem is posed by the West Berlin piece: it was excavated at Amarna, yet it shows evidence of having been made earlier. The slightly upturned nose suggests this, as well as the other details cited. However, there is enough material from Tut-ankh-Amun's tomb and the Hermopolis reliefs to show that artists working in a more traditional mode were present at Amarna. Clearly, our no. 29 belongs to the style of Amarna. The two pieces in the Louvre are very close, especially the face of E 11153. West Berlin no. 553 (Inv. 22621), found at Amarna, is related to the art of Amenophis III as is, probably, East Berlin 20001.

All the inscribed versions appeal to Thoth of Hermopolis, the city lying west across the river from Amarna. Perhaps a local workshop was located here, attempting to work in the new fashion of Amarna, but trained under the old school of Amenophis III. The only hint given by Akhenaten for the selection of the vast plain at Amarna for the new capital was its emptiness and its virginity. It is perhaps more than a coincidence that Hermopolis, lying directly across the river, was the principal seat of a god who, at the same time, represented primeval aspects of the sun, the deity of Amarna, and writing—and in this case, a new writing for a new conception of god.

Minute as it is, this statuette must be compared with other sculptures in the exhibition that show a god representing or protecting man: especially, of course, Chephren and Horus (no. 6), Psamtik and Hathor (no. 38), and, abstractly, Akhenaten and his family (no. 28). Mycerinus with Hathor (no. 7) presents the deity as peer of the king. A large-scale version of the scribe and Thoth is *Cat. gén.* 42162 (*Manuel* III, pl. 150, 3), a Ramesside statue. Thoth, in the form of a baboon, here rests on the head of the scribe (*cf.* Chephren, no. 6).

The material of no. 29 has been called steatite by other writers. Steatite is usually white, although sometimes black; serpentine, usually black or green, is more likely the stone from which the figures were carved. For these materials, see Lucas, pp. 420 f.

E.L.B.T.

30 Tut-ankh-Amun

Catalogue général 42091

With the restoration of the cult of Amun to its rightful place at Thebes, the style of Egyptian sculpture returned to a more normal character. Mannerisms introduced in such sculptures as no. 25 of the reign of Amenophis III are, however, leavened with a touch of naturalism derived from the Amarna experiments. The statue of Tut-ankh-Amun represents the king once more in the traditional pose and garment: standing with left foot forward, he holds both hands flat against a trapezoidal skirt on which hangs what is probably meant to be an apron of beads. Here he wears the traditional *nemes* headcloth with the uraeus springing from the upper edge of the head band.

Although the brows are in relief and the upper lids in semi-relief, the eyes have a naturalistic, hooded quality which sits well with the full, sensitive, slightly down-turned lips. The muscles pucker slightly at the corners of the mouth and recede realistically into the chin. The brows broaden slightly at the point of the curve and end in a point at the outer corner of the eye, as is typical of late Eighteenth Dynasty sculpture. Missing from the eyes, however, is the double upper lid which is frequently found in sculpture from the later part of the reign of Amenophis III and occasionally thereafter. The mouth is outlined with a thin ridge of relief, the head is shifted slightly forward, a memory of the Amarna period, and the neck bears the characteristic lines of fleshy folds. Both ears are pierced and flattened somewhat against the headcloth. The collar bones are discretely and realistically carved.

The torso is distinctly reminiscent of the Amarna period with low breasts widely separated and a little soft. The abdomen retains a slight protuberance and roundness, a feature, which, beginning at the end of the reign of Amenophis III, had become extreme during the time of Akhenaten. The belt, reinscribed by Haremheb, hangs low under the belly. The shoulders and upper arms are schematically rendered, but some care has been taken to indicate the muscles below the elbows whilst the structure of the legs is indifferently treated.

Despite the sensitive, rather impressionistic treatment of the face, the statue as a whole has a formal, academic air about it. The work is clearly an official statement of the restoration of the true royal image as it was meant to be before the heresy of Amarna. In Tut-ankh-Amun's tomb the style of Amarna has a stronger influence; in this statue meant for the temple of Karnak, the principal site of the cult of the now

restored state god Amun, the temple sculptors have succeeded in regaining the dignity of an earlier time without losing entirely the naturalism of the Amarna interlude.

From the Karnak cachette, red granite, late Eighteenth Dynasty, height 145 cm., height of base 11.5 cm., length of base 52.5 cm. Partially restored.

BIBLIOGRAPHY: Vandier, *Manuel* III, pp. 363–5, pl. 117, 1; Lange and Hirmer, *Egypt*, pl. 192. *ASAE* 38 (1938), 23 ff., pl. V.

COMMENTS: The impressionistic quality of this face is remarkable considering the hard stone in which it is carved. More successful perhaps is a sandstone head in Boston (11.1533, W. S. Smith, *Ancient Egypt*, fig. 90; *Manuel*, III, pl. 117, 2). The more malleable material readily lent itself to the sculptor's desire. Despite the formality of the statue of Tut⸗ankh⸗Amun, it is related closely to the more naturalistic yellow steatite statue of Akhenaten, made late in the latter's reign, in Paris, Aldred, *Akhenaten*, pl. I. The headcloth of our statue covers the forehead, a feature typical of late Eighteenth Dynasty sculpture, beginning at least with the reign of Amenophis III. The double upper lid and contoured lips are discussed by Bothmer, 'Private Sculpture of Dynasty XVIII in Brooklyn', *The Brooklyn Museum Annual* 8 (1966–1967) 81, especially nos. 41–42.

E.L.B.T.

31 The Wife of Nakht-Min

Catalogue général 779B

Few sculptures of women from ancient Egypt are as seducingly beautiful as this anonymous lady of the late Eighteenth Dynasty. Her pensive face is almost hidden by an enormous wig, the mass of which is lightened by the elaborate coiffure. Wide tresses are elegantly curled in relief and gathered at the bottom in corkscrew curls. An additional coiled tress lies closely beside each cheek. Across her forehead is a wide diadem composed of an upper register of pomegranates and a lower one of floral ornament. In the centre is a large lotus blossom on either side of which are unopened buds. The stalks are bound together and extend over the top of the head. A wide band, possibly of cloth or gold, lies under the stalks and it was meant, perhaps, to hold the hair in place beneath the narrow stalks. The pressure of the band naturalistically depresses the centre of the wig. Another band (of gold?) holds the hair in place at the level of the jaw. Around her neck is a broad collar of six registers. On her left wrist is a beaded bracelet. One of the remarkable features of the sculpture is the undercutting of the wig around the cheeks.

A pleated gown forms a second skin on her body. The torso is an astonishing realization in stone of human flesh and was never excelled in ancient Egyptian art except in a fragmentary triad of Mycerinus in Boston. The breasts are small, almost like those of a girl, but they are low and protrude outward slightly in the manner of a more mature woman. The nipples are scratched in almost as an afterthought. The muscles of the abdomen undulate beneath the skin-tight dress and the high hip-bones are modelled in great detail. The dress is caught under the right breast and discretely knotted. In her hand, the lady holds a collar made of almost spherical beads, perhaps of gold, on top of which hangs a *menit*-shaped counterpoise. The circular end is incised with a rosette composed of alternating flowers and buds. The right arm, almost entirely destroyed, reaches out to grasp her husband.

The chic coiffure covers an unexpectedly sensitive and expressive face. Vandier has described her eyes as 'lost in a dream'. The upper lids are heavy and are emphasized by sharply incised lines which mould the lids into a realistic shape. The lower lids are in relief. Within the lids the eyes are incised, especially deeply under the upper lids, where the incisions achieve a degree of undercutting. Although the brows are in relief, the relief is slight which gives the impression of plastic or moulded brows. The lips are rather full, especially the lower one. The muscles bunch thoughtfully at the corners of the mouth. The delicate neck has those folds on the throat which had become fashionable in the late Eighteenth Dynasty; here they are modelled rather than incised. The eyes, nose, and mouth have been deliberately mutilated in some purge we know nothing about.

The pensive, rather melancholic expression of the face is characteristic of the end of the Eighteenth Dynasty, and is found in the royal images of the time, *e.g.* Tut-ankh-Amun (no. 30). This image is a far cry from the triumphant sculptures of Tuthmosis III (no. 22) and Amenophis II (no. 23). The skin-tight gown recalls a poem of the New Kingdom, perhaps first written in the Eighteenth Dynasty:

> My lover, it is pleasant to go to the pond in order to bathe myself in thy presence, that I may let thee see my beauty in my tunic of finest white linen, when it is wet. . . .

Here is a rare literary comment on a direct observation of nature that was expressed in the visual arts.

See also Colour Plate VII.

Provenance unknown, late Eighteenth Dynasty, indurated limestone with traces of black and red paint, height 85 cm.

BIBLIOGRAPHY: *5000 Years Catalogue*, London, pl. XVII; Vandier, *Manuel* III, pp. 443, 491, 501, 520, pl. 145, 5; Smith, *Art and Architecture*, pl. 113 B; Aldred, *Akhenaten*, pl. 64; Yoyotte, *Treasures of the Pharaohs*, p. 136 (colour).

COMMENTS: The inscription on the back pillar does not name the lady. However, the head of her husband (*Cat. gén.* 779 A) which formed part of the group statue preserves his name, Nakht-Min, plus the title 'King's Son of . . .', which is broken after the *n*. The restoration of this title has been much discussed, most recently by Aldred, *op. cit.*, pp. 92–3 and 262, n. 14. He prefers to read 'King's Son of [his loins]' which would make Nakht-Min the legitimate son of a king, whom Aldred believes to be Ay. Schulman, *JARCE* 4 (1965) 63, wishes to restore 'King's Son of (Kush)', the title held by the Viceroys of Kush during the New Kingdom, but which did not always imply that the incumbent was in fact a royal heir. Aldred rejects the theory on the basis of Reisner's listing of the Viceroys of Kush, which does not provide for an additional person at this point. A General Nakht-Min contributed shawabtis to the tomb of Tut-ankh-Amun, and Aldred believes the 'King's Son' Nakht-Min and General Nakht-Min to be identical.

The style of Nakht-Min and his wife and their contemporaries is discussed in full by Vandier, *op. cit.*, pp. 519 ff.; the heavy wig, pp. 490 ff.; the costume, pp. 501 f. A very fine and important block statue, made in the same material as that of the Nakht-Min group, has recently come to light and confirms the dating of our sculpture to the period immediately following the reign of Tut-ankh-Amun, Bothmer, 'Private Sculpture of Dynasty XVIII in Brooklyn', *The Brooklyn Museum Annual* 8 (1966–1967), pp. 84 ff., figs. 30–34; Aldred, *Akhenaten*, pl. 66. The block statue bears the cartouches of King Ay; the style is exactly like that of Nakht-Min (although not so precisely refined); the eyes and nose have been mutilated in the same way. See Bothmer, *op. cit.*, for additional discussion of the style and its details.

In a very similar but royal bust of the Ramesside period, the diadem, collar, bracelet, and *menit* are painted yellow to represent gold; the necklace held in the hand, also comprised of spherical beads, is painted blue (*Cat. gén.* 600; Yoyotte, *Treasures of the Pharaohs*, colour plate on p. 145).

The poem is quoted from A. Erman and A. M. Blackman, *The Literature of the Ancient Egyptians*, p. 243.

E.L.B.T.

32 Ramesses II

Catalogue général 616

Only the bust is preserved of what was probably a seated statue of Ramesses the Great. He wears a wig of echeloned curls, a form of head-covering popular in his reign. That it is a wig and not a stylized representation of hair is apparent from the headband lying below it on the forehead, to hold his own hair in place. A diadem, bearing the uraeus, encircles the wig. The hood of the cobra begins to swell at the lower edge of the wig and the coils lie on the diadem. From the back of the head two extensions of the diadem swing back toward the cheeks, one on each side and each bearing a finial in the form of a uraeus crowned with the sun disk. The king wears a type of dress that was particularly favoured at this time. On the upper part of his body, he wears a tunic, the right sleeve of which is flared and pleated below the shoulder. Over the left part of the bust is thrown what is apparently a pleated shawl. In the complete examples the flared right sleeve ends above the elbow, while the shawl covers the left arm to the wrist. Either the tunic or the shawl—it is not clear which—is tied under the right breast. A bracelet in the form of the *wedjat*, the Sacred Eye of Horus, adorns the right wrist and the hand holds a *heka* sceptre against the chest. A broad collar of several rows of beads ending in petal-shaped pendants hangs on the king's breast.

The face is small, delicate, and youthful. The almond-shaped eyes are reminiscent of the late Eighteenth Dynasty with their hooded, relief-edged upper lids and the incised lines which mark the roots of the lids. The brows are in high relief and follow the curves of the eyes. Long cosmetic lines in relief increase the length of the eyes. The mouth is small but the lips are full and outlined by a thin ridge of relief. The sculptor was attentive to the modelling of the torso: even the left breast is delineated beneath the heavy pleats of the tunic.

The concept of kingship as represented by this sculpture shows how far the Egyptians had gone from the heady days of the first half of the Eighteenth Dynasty. We have seen the melancholy of the end of the Dynasty in the statue of Tut-ankh-Amun. Now the king is triumphant again, but he is triumphant in the form of a very human man who affects even a fancy court gown. The wig, although there are one or two royal prototypes in the Eighteenth Dynasty, must be related to the old hair style of private personalities in the Old Kingdom. The rather prettified features suggest fashionableness rather than the dignity of the king as god. Here is a king who has stepped down from his lofty perch to become a leader among peers. Even

the bombast of his colossal monuments at Abu Simbel does not escape an imputation of a man acting in the role of god rather than being god.

From Tanis in the Delta, Nineteenth Dynasty, black granite, height 82.5 cm., width from broken right arm 64 cm.

BIBLIOGRAPHY: *PM* IV, p. 22; *Tel*, pl. 142; Vandier, *Manuel* III, pp. 394, 396, 409, 413, 415, pl. 126, 2; Kodansha, pl. 80 (colour).

COMMENTS: The closest parallel to the Tanis bust is the great statue of Ramesses II in Turin (*Manuel* III, pl. 126, 1, 3; Yoyotte, *Treasures of the Pharaohs*, pl. on p. 143 and p. 144, where Yoyotte states that the inscription is original and not usurped by Ramesses II). Vandier, *op. cit.*, p. 394, places the Turin and Tanis statues in his first group of sculptures of Ramesses II, which represents the king in his earlier years. A colossal head of Ramesses II wearing a wig like that of the Tanis head is in Boston (89.558 from Bubastis, also in the Delta; *Manuel* III, pl. 127, 2). See Vandier, *op. cit.*, pp. 392 ff., for detailed discussion of the sculptures of Ramesses II, particularly pp. 412–13 for the costume worn by the Turin and Tanis statues, and p. 409 for the wig of the Tanis bust. For an exceptional example of the round wig on a private person of the Eighteenth Dynasty, see Bothmer, 'Private Sculpture of Dynasty XVIII in Brooklyn', *The Brooklyn Museum Annual* 8 (1966–1967), pp. 67–8, figs. 13–16, and n. 23 (p. 67).

E.L.B.T.

33 Dancers at a Funeral

Journal d'Entrée 4872

This remarkable scene shows a dance taking place at the funeral of some unknown man of the Nineteenth Dynasty. On the right, leading the procession in which the sarcophagus is presumably being carried, are eight men dressed in various costumes. Those on the far right wear a long, sleeved and pleated garment and long hair hanging over their shoulders. The next group wears a long skirt only, with the same trapezoidal front tied at the waist as the group on the right. This second group has shaven heads. The arms of these six figures are raised, but the sculptor has not indicated the raised left arms of the central group, the arms being lost behind those of the first group. To the left are two men in short kilts. The figure in the foreground has a tripartite tassel or flap hanging between his legs. The same figure carries a staff with a flanged end. The movement of the legs of all these figures indicates that they are running forward, unless they are meant to be engaged in some simple-stepped dance. To indicate the movement of the back legs of the second group, the ankles are bent at an unnatural angle, so as not to confuse them with the legs of the first group. The sculptor means to show that the groups are in a single rank, the figures on the far right being in front of the viewer, with the others grouped behind them. Only two errors have crept into this suggestion of 'perspective' (which excludes, of course, the true perspective of a vanishing point): the pleated sleeve of the farther figure of the first group is drawn to meet the upraised arm of the first man in the central group; and the staff is carved in front of the arms of the central group instead of behind them. The faces of the first and last groups are deeply lined, as if in grief. Inscriptions around the central group name two of the participants: Khai and Nakhti, without specifying which men are indicated.

The left half of the relief is occupied by a scene of extraordinary animation. Eight women and two girls dance excitedly to the music of tambourines and castanets. Two ranks of women playing the tambourine wear long transparent gowns. Their hair, held in place by fillets, is long and arranged so that it hangs over both shoulders. The first woman in the front rank, however, has her hair cut short. All apparently wear disk-shaped earrings, although in one or two cases they are not shown. All the women, with two exceptions, turn their heads toward the arriving sarcophagus. In the back or upper rank, the leading woman turns her head back, as does the last figure in the front rank. In both cases, the hair flies out on both sides of the head, as if in the very act of turning quickly in a step of the dance. Another woman in the front rank

twists her body, while her head continues to face the principal scene, now missing. The remaining figures are two small naked girls in early adolescence, still wearing the curious locks on otherwise shaven heads typical of Egyptian youth, but showing the small, highly placed breasts of early womanhood. They dance vigorously with a pair of castanets, probably made of bone or ivory, in each hand. They are arranged symmetrically in front of the short-haired woman, but the slightly differing movements of their feet and castanets prevent the symmetry from slowing the pace of the urgent movement of the entire scene.

The carving is characteristic of much relief of the Nineteenth Dynasty. If looked at closely, it appears a little careless, rather hurried, somewhat impressionistic. Its success lies in the total scene rather than in specific detail. Yet affecting detail is not lacking, as in the case of the lines of grief in the faces of the male mourners. The sketchy carving is entirely suitable to the rapidity of the movement of the subject.

From Saqqara, found in 1859 apparently re-used in the Serapeum, Nineteenth Dynasty, limestone, height about 55 cm., length 105 cm.

Bibliography: *PM* III, p. 202; Vandier, *Manuel*, IV, pp. 444 ff., fig. 237 with other references; *Tel*, pl. 150; Kodansha, pl. 83 (colour).

Comments: Vandier, *op. cit.*, has pointed out that the funerary dance shown here has a secular character. Stylistically, the relief is derived from work like the more carefully executed tomb of Haremheb (end of the Eighteenth Dynasty), Lange and Hirmer, *Egypt*, pls. 206–9. The tall, lean figures are typical of the private tombs erected at Saqqara in the Ramesside period. The style finds its origins ultimately in the Amarna period. *Cf.*, *e.g.*, the mourners' deep cheek grooves with that of Akhenaten, no. 26. The Ramesside innovations in the use of space are discussed in full by W. S. Smith, *Interconnections in the Ancient Near East*, chapter 7.

E.L.B.T.

34 The Cats serving Lady Mouse

probably Journal d'Entrée 31199

In the pastoral world of the ancient Egyptians, the animal kingdom played an important role in religious thought and in daily life. The charm of the observation of nature is revealed in the tiny fragment of birds at play from Weserkaf's temple (no. 8) and the enormous significance of the animal symbol in religion is portrayed by the great cow of Hathor protecting a man named Psamtik (no. 38). From the Twentieth Dynasty town of workmen at the necropolis of Deir el Medina at Thebes have come numerous sketches on limestone flakes showing animals engaged in various pursuits. In the papyrus fragment exhibited here we find cats and mice assuming the roles of humans in a reversal of the animals' true status. In a satire on the human condition, the cats have been charged with caring for the mice as servitors. On the left a mouse attired in the elegant gown of a lady of the court sits on a wicker stool, resting her feet on a high footrest and quaffing a glass of wine, while a lady cat dresses Lady Mouse's fashionable coiffure. The cat herself wears a tress of black hair held in place by a chic pin. In front of the mouse another cat holds what was probably a jug of wine. Farther along a small nursemaid kitten carries a baby mouse in a sling. Behind them another cat holds a fan or sunshade over the little ones while carrying a jug of liquid with its other hand. The right side of the papyrus shows the enemies of the barnyard, the foxes, feeding their prey. One fox carries jugs of food on a yoke, one of which has been removed by a second fox who pours the contents in a trough for the penned cattle. A loose fragment shows part of a third fox carrying what appears to be a sheaf of wheat from a granary scene.

Throughout, most of the animals are outlined in black over faint red drawing lines, and occasionally the black is thickened to produce spatial illusionism, as in the cases of the heavier foreground ears of the cat nursemaid and cupbearer. The backs are a wash of light tan, the markings of fur indicated by very light strokes of grey over which are placed small chevrons, almost half-moon shaped, of heavier grey. The stomachs are white with a red outline over which dashes of black break up the outline, to create an illusion of light falling on the fur. The lady mouse is outlined in red except for the grey head, face and neck, surrounded by black outlines. The foxes are coloured like the cats, but the colours are somewhat stronger than those of the latter. The horns of the black and white cow are blue, as is the feeding trough. Because of the black paper on which the papyrus is mounted, the horns and trough appear to be blue and black.

The history of the later Twentieth Dynasty is one of troubles for Egypt. Clearly the satire illustrated here, amusing and charming as it is, is meant to be a bitter comment on the reversal of the proper roles of men in a disintegrating society. The irony recalls the literature of the end of the Old Kingdom and early Middle Kingdom, when men lamented the high positions of those who had been nothing and the loss of fortune by those formerly of wealth and power.

Apparently purchased at Tuna el Gebel, probably Twentieth Dynasty, painting on papyrus, length of larger piece 40.5 cm., height 13 cm.

BIBLIOGRAPHY: E. Brugsch, *ÄZ* 35 (1897) 140 f. and pl. I; M. Gauthier-Laurent, *Melanges Maspero* I (*MIFAO* 66 [1935–38]) 684 and pl. II D; *Tel*, pl. 163; Smith, *Art and Architecture*, pp. 235 f., pl. 170 A; Kodansha, pl. 85 (colour).

COMMENTS: See W. S. Smith, *op. cit.*, for discussion of this papyrus and similar examples. For the dating, see especially Smith, p. 235, n. 21 (on p. 284). In the famous papyrus of Turin, in which the erotic scenes involve a priest and concubines and may themselves be satirical in nature, a separate part of the papyrus illustrates various animal groups, including a mouse playing the role of a Ramesside king in his chariot attacking a fortress manned by cats. A well-known papyrus in the British Museum (Smith, *op. cit.*, pl. 170 B) shows foxes and cats herding gazelles and ducks as well as a cat attending a seated mouse. An ostrakon from Deir el Medina has a cat herding ducks (Cairo, *J. d'E.* 63801). See R. Würfel, 'Die ägyptische Fabel in Bildkunst und Literatur', *Wissenschaftliche Zeitschrift der Universität Leipzig* 1952/53, Heft 3, pp. 63–77, 153–60 (I have not been able to consult this work).

The *Journal d'Entrée* of the Egyptian Museum is uncertain about the number and provenance of the papyrus.

For scenes of the dressing of hair, see Gauthier-Laurent, *op. cit.*, pp. 673 ff.

E.L.B.T.

35 Here-ubekhet enters the Fields of the Blessed

14-7/35-6

In the Twenty-first Dynasty the rule of Egypt was divided between the high priests of Amun at Thebes and a dynasty of kings at Tanis in the Delta. The high priests sometimes took to themselves the dignities of kingship and even occasionally enclosed their names in the royal cartouche. The troubled times led to experiments in religious practice, a case in point being the Book of the Dead. In the Eighteenth Dynasty this collection of spells for guiding the deceased through the perils of the underworld consisted of lengthy texts accompanied by more or less elaborate illustrations. By the Twenty-first Dynasty pictorial details had replaced more and more of the text until the latter had become highly abbreviated. The papyrus of the 'Chantress of Amun' Here-ubekhet seems to be such an abbreviated Book of the Dead or what, with its glossy illustrations, has been called an *edition de luxe*.

The papyrus is meant to be read textually and visually from the right. At the beginning is a great presentation scene in which Here-ubekhet, adorned with a cone of scented grease and lotus bud, makes offerings to the funerary god Ptah-Sokar wearing the mummiform shroud of his role as a manifestation of Osiris. Behind him stands the goddess Isis. In front of the god stands a striped column on which hangs an emblematic leopard skin, a fetish of Anubis, god of the necropolis. The pile of offerings is executed with the greatest refinement. Four offering stands are heaped with foods and plants, including joints of meat, squash, breads, lotus blossoms and grape leaves. A stylized garland of petals, reminiscent of the jewelled broad collar (*cf.* no. 31), surrounds the offering stands. The grape leaves and squash are treated with exceptional realism, especially the squash, the markings of which curve to suggest its rounded form. The inscription above the offerings first names Ptah-Sokar-Osiris and Isis, then proceeds with Here-ubekhet's name, titles (she was also a priestess in the Temple of Mut at Karnak) and her genealogy. She was the daughter of a certain priestess named Isis-em-Kheb, who in turn was the daughter of the High Priest of Amun, Men-kheper-Ra.

In the next scene the priestess kneels on a stepped platform. On the left Ra-Horus and on the right Thoth purify the lady with ritual vessels from which flow streams of the *ankh* (the hieroglyphic sign for 'life') and the *was* (the sign meaning 'to have dominion'). The large inscription facing Here-ubekhet refers to the 'Opening of the Mouth', an essential part of the purification ritual of the deceased. The gods state that she

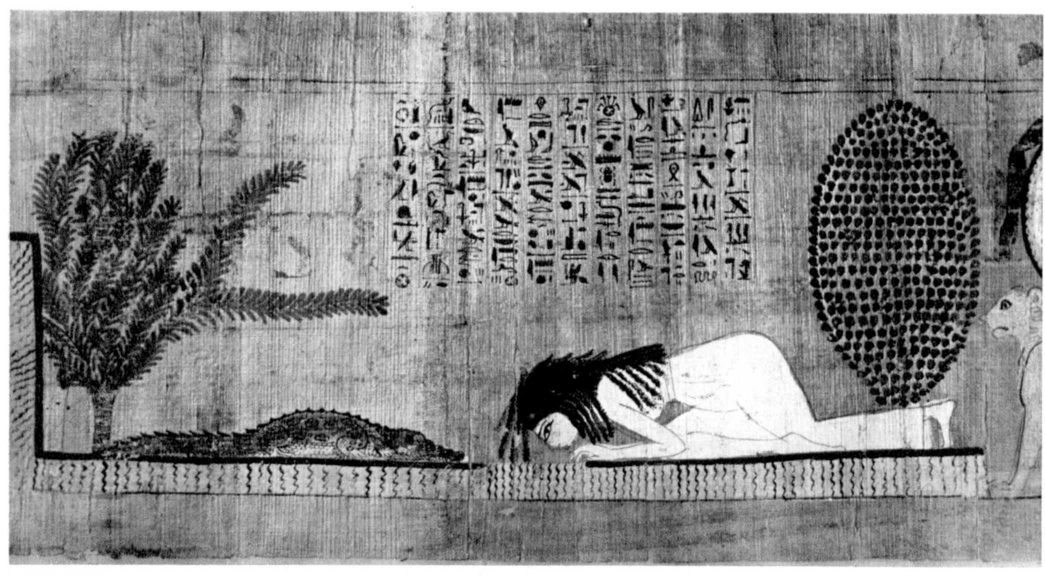

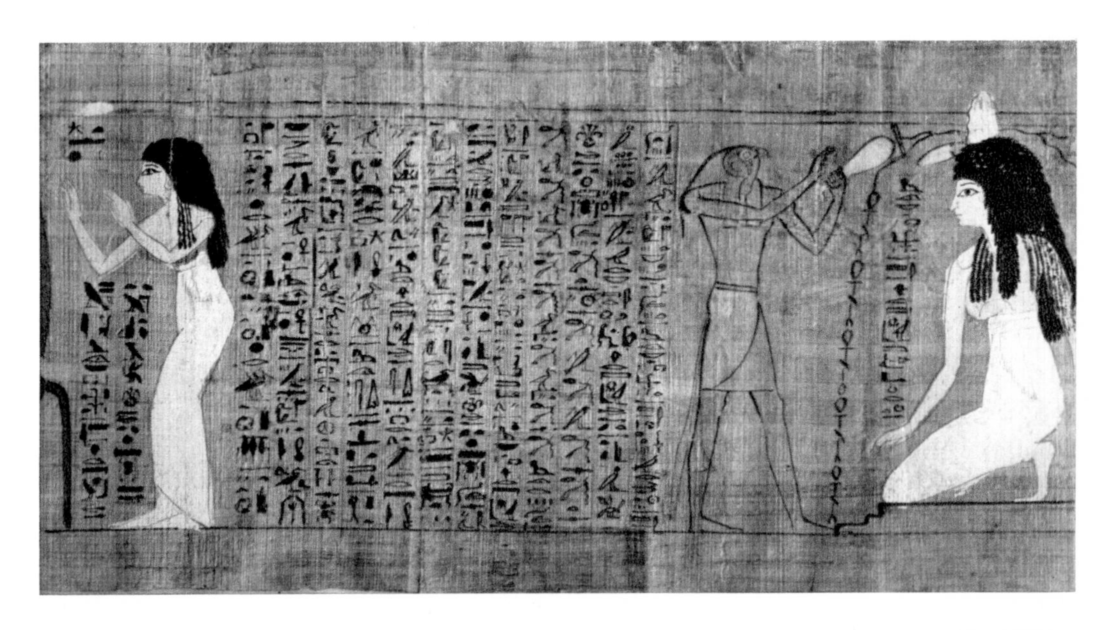

is pure and she shall come to them, to which she replies: 'I have come toward the gods who are in the sky....'

The next vignette shows the youthful sun-god seated within the disk of the sun, encircled by a serpent biting its tail, apparently a symbol of the sun's eternity. The disk is supported by two lions representing the horizon and the bucranium of Hathor in her aspect as an ancient sun-goddess. The heavenly counterpart of the earthly support is given by the goddess Nut, whose breasts and arms grasp the disk from above. The greeter of the sun, the baboon, holds out the protective Eye of Horus at this critical moment of the sun's rebirth, and behind him stands Here-ubekhet, her arms raised in greeting.

The following scene is one of great poetry. The inscription begins with two columns addressed by the earth-god Geb, which face the supplicant. The remainder of the inscription is read from the left.

Below, Here-ubekhet kneels on the black earth of the river's edge to drink the pure water, her hair falling loosely over her face. Before her lies the crocodile which represents the god Geb. The scene is framed on the right by a stylized sycamore tree and on the left by a somewhat more naturalistically rendered poplar. The channel or river turns upward, then curves gently down to meet the ground line of the painting. Only at the point where the lady drinks from the waters is the black border of earth broken. The final scene is the ultimate goal of the now purified deceased: the Fields of Yaru or the Fields of the Blessed, where eternal harvests will provide sustenance forever. Above, moving along the curving line of the riverbank, a man ploughs the black earth with a pair of oxen (the second barely indicated by a few lines). The bewhiskered plougher turns his head to watch Here-ubekhet sow the seeds from a basket. Below, the temporal sequence separated by the abrupt line of the river, the harvest is reaped. Here-ubekhet's companion reaches his arm around a sheaf of grain, cutting it with a flint-toothed sickle. The lady bends down to gather the cut grain.

The papyrus is arranged in episodic scenes. The white body of Here-ubekhet forms, however, an important unifying factor throughout the long papyrus. It is also to be noted that, although the general orientation is from right to left, the last scene faces to the right, thus emphasizing its finality: it is so placed that Here-ubekhet may keep in view her goal, the Fields of the Blessed.

See also Colour Plate VIII.

From Deir el Bahari, 'Papyrus 133', Twenty-first Dynasty (about 1000 BC or slightly later), painting on papyrus, length 198 cm., greatest height about 23.8 cm.

BIBLIOGRAPHY: A. Piankoff, 'Les deux papyrus "mythologique" de Her-ouben au Musée du Caire', *ASAE* 49 (1949) 129 ff., pls. 1–12; A. Piankoff, *Mythological Papyri*, pp. 71–4 and foldout pl. 1; *Tel*, pls. 159–61; Yoyotte, *Treasures of the Pharaohs*, p. 178 and colour pl. on p. 179; Kodansha, pl. 86 (colour).

COMMENTS: The texts quoted here are from Piankoff, *Mythological Papyri*. The poplar was identified as *salix safsaf* by Keimer, see *ASAE* 49 (1949) 134 and n. 4. We are ill-informed about monumental painting in the Twenty-first Dynasty. Most of the documents are in the form of papyri or vignettes on mummy cases. In general, we might define the work of the period as 'hard-edge' painting, and such is the overall quality of Here-ubekhet's painting. However, a more painterly instinct creeps into details, such as the white wash of the bodies and the loosely arranged locks of hair. The style is a descendant of the Twentieth Dynasty painting, no. 34 (see the references there cited in Comments). The second papyrus of Here-ubekhet appears to be by a different, but no less skilful hand. Ranke, *Personnamen*, p. 253 (6) gives *hryt-wbht*.

E.L.B.T.

36 Hor-em-akhet, son of King Shabaka

Catalogue général 42204

Surprisingly, the Kushite conquerors of Egypt in the eighth century BC brought about a resurgence of artistic activity and achievement unequalled since early Ramesside times. The Sudan itself had felt Egyptian influence from the Old Kingdom onward and during the Middle and New Kingdoms this influence was particularly strong. The origins of the Kushite house of the eighth century are obscure, but their works at the temple of Amun at Gebel Barkal near the Sudanese capital of Napata demonstrate their complete acquaintance with Egyptian style and manners. Hor-em-akhet was a son of one of these foreign rulers of Egypt, Shabaka, and he held the position of High Priest of Amun at Thebes during the reigns of Shabaka's successors Taharqa and Tanwetamani. Hor-em-akhet was evidently a half-brother of Taharqa, placed in high position at Thebes to consolidate Kushite power there. Until Taharqa's reign, the kings themselves seem to have spent little time in Egypt, preferring to rule through their viceroys (*cf.* no. 37). While Taharqa resided in the Delta it was no doubt politic to have one of the royal family in a leading post at Thebes.

The southern caste of the royal prince is seen at first glance in the wide cheek bones, full mouth, and broad nostrils. In every other respect the sculpture is purely Egyptian, even to the point of being carved in red quartzite to imitate the traditional Egyptian colour for men. A broad collar in relief lies around his neck and over the collar lies a chain from which hangs an *ankh* sign, also in high relief. He wears the royal *shendyt* kilt and his head is shaven. Folds in the throat are modelled and emphasized with incised lines. The structure of the skull is delineated with a ridge across the top of the cranium and the slope of the cranium meets the sides of the skull to form a triangle. Other sharp angles join the cranium to the low forehead. An unusual, possibly unique, plastic bulge encircles the back of the skull, ending as ridges below the tips of the ears. This detail may represent the point where bone and membrane meet behind the ears. The angularity is repeated in the shape of the eyes and brows; the brows and upper lids are in relief. As in the late Eighteenth Dynasty and Ramesside Period, the root of the upper lid is sharply incised. Other incised lines delineate the outer swell of the nostrils. Discrete grooves curve downward around the corners of the mouth. The philtrum is barely indicated. The jaw juts forward, in effect pushing back the cheeks, so that the profile of the cheeks does not intrude over the nose. The modelling of the torso is restrained and has the bipartite form that is particularly characteristic of sculpture of the Twenty-fifth Dynasty: a deep

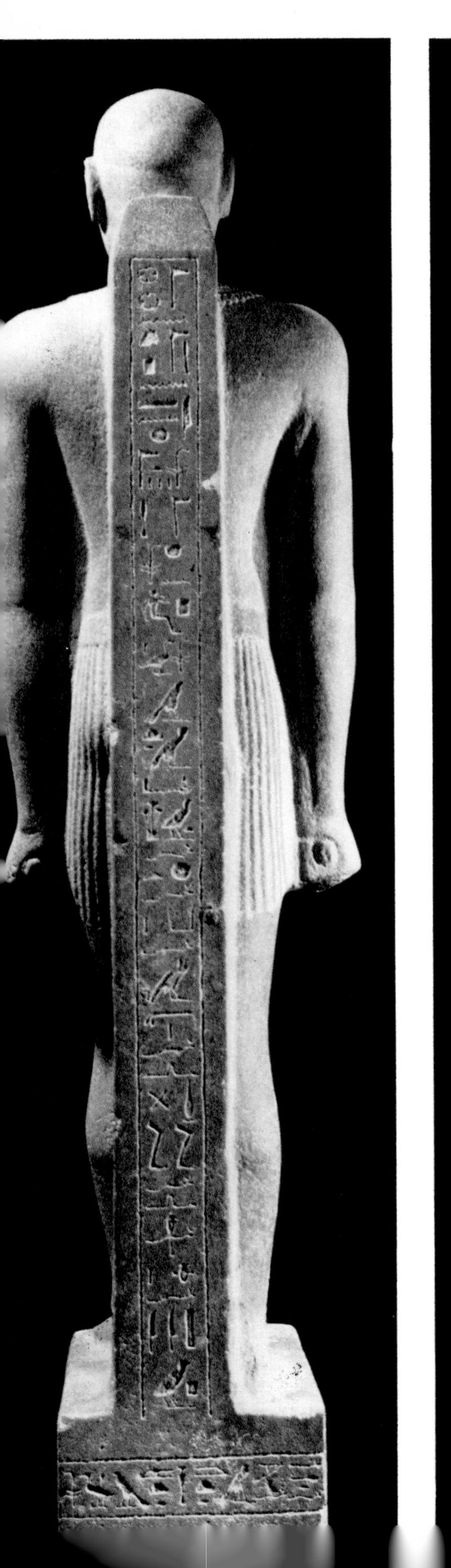

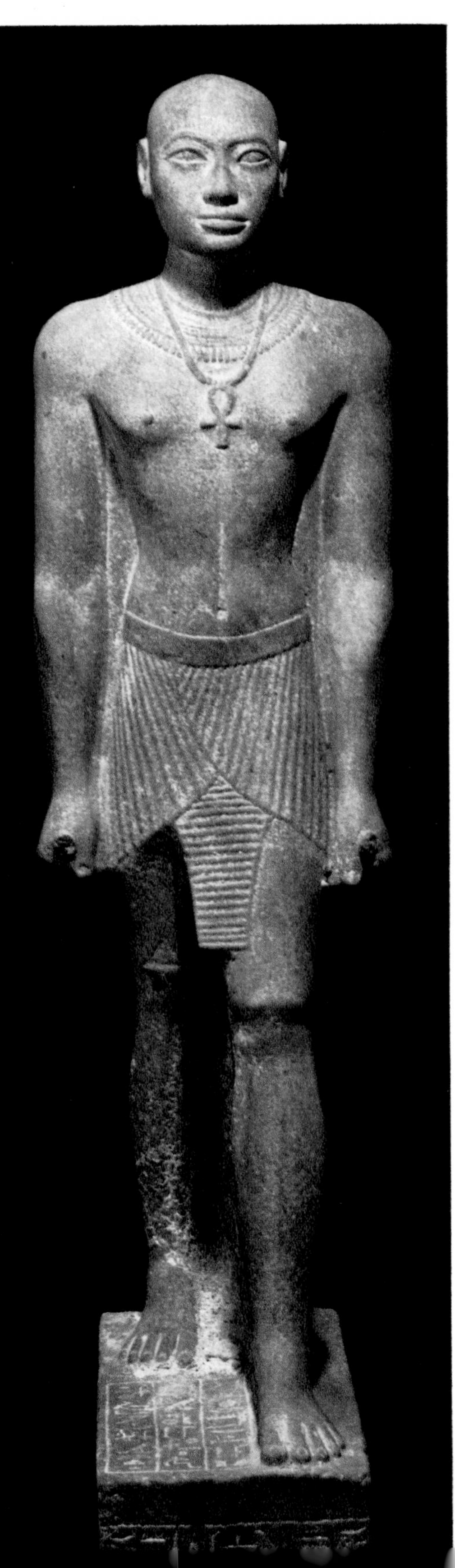

groove extends from the navel upward to meet the *ankh* sign, thereby dividing the torso into two halves. When an element like the *ankh* is not present, the groove continues into the sternal depression above the breasts. The legs, on the other hand, are treated with some detail. The triangular form of the tensed right knee-cap is exaggerated. In the more relaxed left leg which steps forward, the knee-cap protrudes outward both from the front and in profile. The ridge extending from knee-cap to ankle is rather more naturalistically rendered here than it often is in Egyptian sculpture. The prominence of the ridge is more often a mannerism of style than it is a fact of nature. The double grooving of the outer leg, again very common in Egyptian sculpture, is conspicuous here. The fat muscle of the inner calf is treated realistically. The arms are summarily rendered, although the muscle below the elbow is distinctive as usual.

The sculptor has not produced a portrait of Hor-em-akhet, despite the skill with which he has caught the essence of the prince's origin. The idiom of the Twenty-fifth Dynasty is an idealizing type produced to represent the physical characteristics of its patrons. The facial features are African: the style itself harks back to earlier times. The influence of the new type, and the changes it wrought, will be seen in the head of Mentuemhat (no. 37).

From the Karnak cachette, Twenty-fifth Dynasty, red quartzite, height 66 cm.

Bibliography: *PM* II, p. 52; *Tel*, pl. 171.

Comments: Although it was left to the Twenty-sixth Dynasty to initiate a true 'renaissance' during which specific features were borrowed from previous periods, already in the Twenty-fifth Dynasty there was a conscious effort to use earlier models. The serious expression of Hor-em-akhet's statue has something of the Middle Kingdom in it, and the shaven head is more typical of Middle Kingdom private statues than those of the Ramesside period during which shaven heads are much rarer in the round than they are in relief (*cf.* no. 33). On the other hand, the treatment of the eyes and the folds of the neck are derived directly from the Eighteenth and Nineteenth Dynasties. B. V. Bothmer, *ESLP*, p. 11, has observed a further connection between Hor-em-akhet's statue and the Middle Kingdom, namely the 'broken' shape of the top of the back pillar, which is found in a Middle Kingdom example (Kansas City 39–8). The bipartite treatment of the torso is itself a Middle Kingdom invention (see *ESLP*, pp. xxxv and 11). An especially typical example of the Twenty-fifth Dynasty is Boston 07.494, where the form of the back pillar is also like Hor-em-akhet's (*ESLP*, no. 9).

The shape of the head has no precise parallels, although the ridge across the cranium is found in MMA 02.4.191 (*ESLP*, no. 7). The hooded eyes, similar to Middle Kingdom work (*cf.* nos. 16–18), are characteristic of much Twenty-fifth Dynasty sculpture (*ESLP*, p. 8).

E.L.B.T.

37 Mentuemhat, Governor of Upper Egypt

Catalogue général 647

While Taharqa controlled the fortunes of Egypt from Tanis in the Delta and Hor-em-akhet (no. 36) the son of Shabaka held the high priesthood of Amun at Thebes, the Fourth Priest of Amun Mentuemhat, a native Egyptian, governed the Upper Egyptian provinces. Throughout the Twenty-fifth Dynasty the Kushite kings preferred to make only occasional visits to Egypt, stamping out revolts and repulsing as best they could attempts by the Assyrians to take control of the country. In Taharqa's reign, Esarhaddon of Assyria did succeed in conquering Egypt and he held it for a time. Taharqa and his successor Tanwetamani attempted to recover the lost territories, but Ashurbanipal defeated these efforts, finally driving the Kushites out of Egypt altogether and sacking Thebes in the process. The foundations were thus laid for the establishment of the Twenty-sixth Dynasty of Sais in the Delta under Psamtik I. During these disastrous times, one man stands out above all others, surviving the Kushite domination, the Assyrian invasions and the founding of the Saite Dynasty: Mentuemhat, whose lowly priestly position in no way reflected his political authority. At least a dozen of his statues have survived and his enormous tomb in the Asasif at Thebes is one of the most notable examples of the art of sculpture in relief in the Late Period.

Several of the statues represent the Governor in the standard idealistic and traditional form. Others illustrate varying degrees of a serious attempt to portray the actual features of Mentuemhat, and of these the present bust is the most successful and exceptional. The heavy, apparently care-worn features give more than a suggestion of an elderly face. The sweeping wig, cut severely back from the forehead, represents the balding head of an old man. The same mannerism can be seen in the hieroglyph of an elderly man leaning on a forked staff in the panel of Hesy-Ra (no. 4). The unusually small eyes are imbedded in heavy rolls of flesh. The upper lid is retracted completely under the roll of the brow, leaving exposed only the outer edge in relief, the outlines of which are incised. This edge of relief continues into the modelled brow, overlapping the lower lid. The brow sweeps in a reverse curve to meet the point of the socket. The cheek bones are strongly defined, but the cheeks themselves are fatty, with deep grooves on either side of the mouth. Deep nasolabial furrows delineate the inner edges of the cheeks and thick folds of flesh lie on either side of the nose, emphasizing the shape of the eye sockets. The hair of the brows is thick, ending in points at the outer corners of the eyes. Above the root of the nose the brows are pinched together, indicated by a sharp

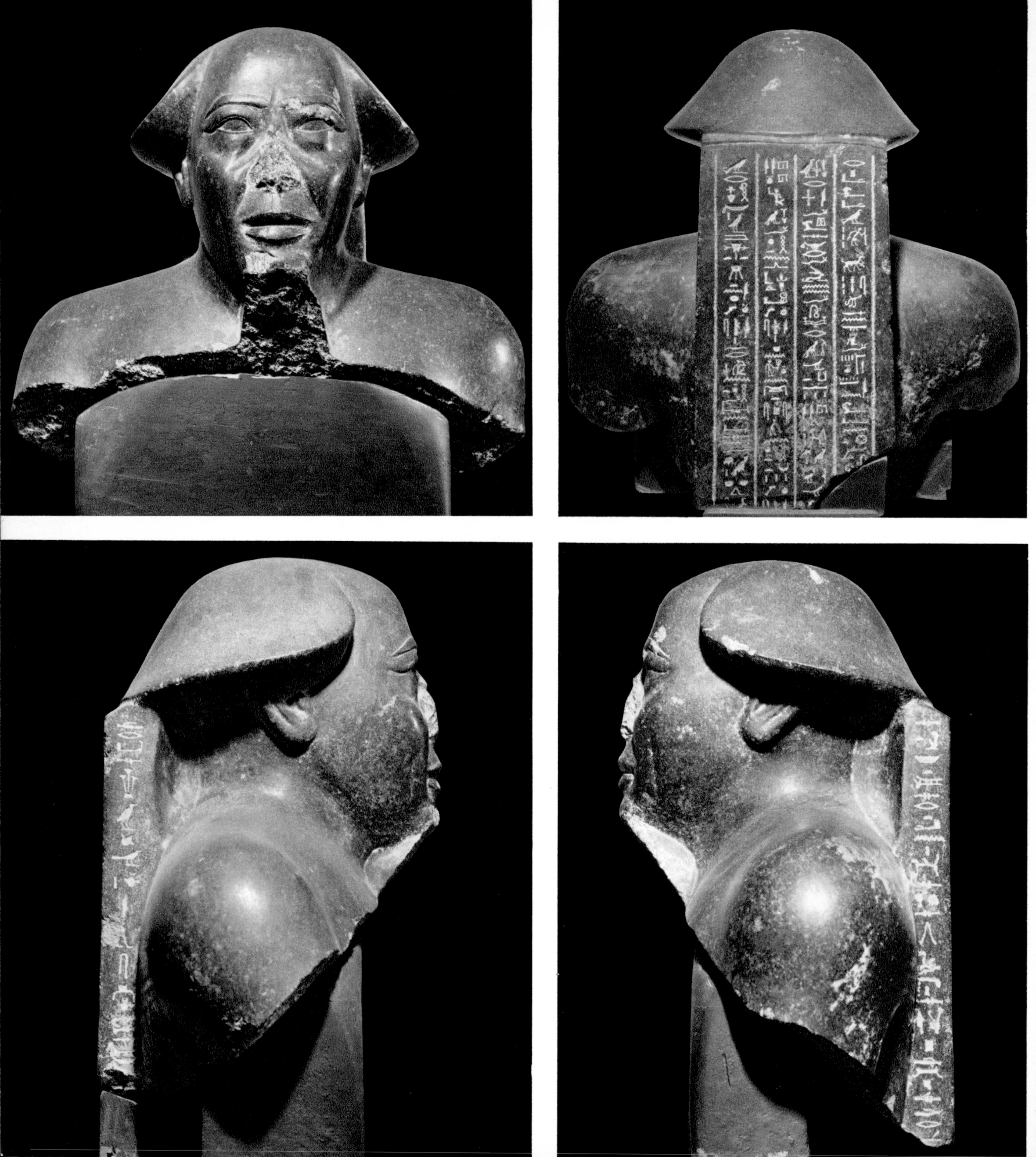

groove above the nose. The philtrum is distinctive and rather long, and the mouth is full. Slight grooves curve downward around the corners of the lower lip. The ear lobes are long, protruding beneath the hair and lying along the angle of the jaw bone. Despite the remarkable attention given to anatomical structure elsewhere, the ears are an almost haphazard afterthought.

As early as the Fourth Dynasty, the Egyptian sculptor produced great portraits (*cf.* the limestone bust of Ankh-haf in Boston, W. S. Smith, *Ancient Egypt*, 1960, fig. 17 in colour), and even the reliefs of Hesy-Ra (no. 4) and Khai-bau-Sokar (no. 5) have some features specific enough to have been taken from the living models. Invariably, these portraits are of older men: Ankh-haf, like Mentuemhat, has a balding head and a face covered with the loose flesh of age. Whereas the modelling and details of the earlier sculpture are restrained in keeping with its time, the master of Mentuemhat's portrait has allowed himself full expression of the details of physiognomy as well as something of the inner spirit of the man. He is stern, grim, and in the free manifestation of his unflattering physical features, perhaps even cynical.

From Karnak, Temple of Mut, early Twenty-sixth Dynasty, black granite, height from bottom of back pillar 48 cm., width between broken arms 47 cm.

BIBLIOGRAPHY: *PM* II, pp. 92–93; Leclant, *Bibliothèque d'Étude, Institut français d'archéologie orientale* 35 (1961) 97 ff., and pls. 25 ff.; Smith, *Art and Architecture*, pp. 348 f. and pl. 183 A; Bothmer, *ESLP*, pp. 15, 17, 25, fig. 29; Kodansha, pl. 104.

COMMENTS: For the monuments of Mentuemhat, see Leclant's study, *op. cit.* The plates of Leclant's work reveal the diversity that exists among the statues. Bothmer, *ESLP*, p. 15, is reluctant to accept our no. 37 as a true portrait, and on p. 17 denies a relationship between the bust and the Kansas City relief of Mentuemhat (*ESLP*, fig. 32). However, several features of the facial anatomy are found on both monuments and it seems clear that there is more than a casual similarity between the two. On the basis of *Cat. gén.* 42236 (Smith, *Art and Architecture*, pl. 183 B) it is possible to suggest that the latter is an earlier version of *Cat. gén.* 647. Even in the idealizing Old Kingdom the sculptor attempted to differentiate the features of old age from those of more youthful maturity (*cf.* Ranofer, Comments, no. 10).

The sharp angle between cranium and forehead has been observed in no. 36. The break under the chin of Mentuemhat's bust is curious but explained by BM 1643 (Leclant, pl. X) and an unnumbered sculpture in Cairo (Leclant, pl. VII). In both pieces Mentuemhat kneels and holds a large stela in front of him. The filling between body and stela extends to a short beard. On the right side of the chin of our no. 37 there is a minute trace of what was probably a beard. The form of the wig is otherwise unknown in the Late Period, but prototypes exist from the New Kingdom: Leclant, pl. XXIX (BM 43132, probably late Eighteenth Dynasty); pl. XXX (Turin 3018, Nineteenth Dynasty); p. 100, n. 1 (Besançon 17–46, said to be time of Amenophis III). Neither the BM nor Turin examples make such dramatic use of this rare form.

The name of Mentuemhat does not occur in the inscriptions, but the bust clearly belongs to him because of the titles which are listed on it. The bust was found with a headless but fully inscribed block statue of Mentuemhat in the Temple of Mut at Karnak (*Cat. gén.* 646). Mentuemhat was in office as late as the fourteenth year of Psamtik I (see *ESLP*, p. 15). We date the bust to the Saite Twenty-sixth Dynasty on the basis of the obvious representation of old age.

E.L.B.T.

38 The Goddess Hathor and the Overseer of Sealers, Psamtik

Catalogue général 784

In earlier periods the Egyptians often enough represented men or kings under the protection of, or in conjunction with, deities in animal form. Only in the Late Period, however, do these zoomorphic deities come to dominate completely such sculptures. Heretofore, the animal had formed, if not a minor aspect of the sculpture, usually at least no more than an equal element. The most notable example is the diorite statue of Chephren (no. 6). The relative insecurity of the times perhaps explains the Late Period's dependence on an all-powerful image of the deity. The texts of the period are full of lengthy appeals to the gods; many of the textual formulae are based on earlier models; and the kings of the Twenty-fifth and Twenty-sixth Dynasties set about the restoration of monuments neglected since the end of the New Kingdom. There is something almost hectic about the period's attempts to establish legitimacy through devotion to its predecessors and piety before the gods.

Psamtik's sculpture has an Eighteenth Dynasty prototype which may well have been the very model on which the later object was based. The earlier example is the well-known statue of Hathor the cow and Amenophis II which stood originally in Tuthmosis III's chapel dedicated to Hathor at Deir el Bahri. It is not impossible that Psamtik or his sculptor saw this statue at Thebes.

The great cow of Hathor strides forward with the left legs, imitating the classical stance of the Egyptian standing male figure. As always, the matrix of the stone fills the space between the legs. This feature inspired the sculptor to employ an unusual device: on both sides of the sculpture the four legs are shown and in each case it is the left legs which step forward. From the right, the right legs, which are in the foreground, are executed in bold relief, almost in the round, while the left legs are in low relief against the filling slab; from the left, the reverse is true. This uncanny logic is wholly successful if we accept the principle of Egyptian sculpture that demanded that the integrity of the cube of stone be respected.

The modelling of the animal is unparalleled. It is a symphony of smoothly undulating planes in which muscle and skeletal structure are worked together as if in a plastic material like clay. The dignity of the stance is enhanced by the forceful head and the purely conventional but strongly defined treatment of the brows. The form of the brows—parallel ridges or wrinkles—is characteristic of ancient Near Eastern art and is found, for example, on the bulls of the Libya Palette (no. 1). Tall horns encircle a feather-crowned

sun disk on which a uraeus raises its head. Again, free spaces are filled with stone; even the ears are carved in relief against heavy buttresses. Around her neck, the cow wears a necklace composed of double barrel-shaped beads with spherical spacers. A *menit*-shaped counterpoise—the emblem of Hathor—lies in relief on the back of the neck.

The small figure of Psamtik is a perfectly realized sculpture in its own right, and the eye is not offended by the fact that the figure is attached to the cow. With poetic licence we might describe the figure of the cow as an elaborate back pillar against which Psamtik stands. He wears a bag wig with small tabs in front of the large ears and a long belted skirt with a rectangular front that forms a background for the carefully spaced and written inscription, listing Psamtik's offices. An undecorated rectangular amulet or pectoral in relief hangs around his neck. The face bears no trace of individuality and has no reference at all to the experiments of a hundred years earlier as represented by nos. 36 and 37.

The tripartite construction of the torso is typical of Late Period sculpture after the earlier part of the Twenty-sixth Dynasty (*cf.* no. 36). The torso is divided into three separate elements: abdomen, rib cage, and breasts, with only a slight depression descending from sternal notch to navel.

In any other culture the sculpture must be labelled bizarre, but it was one of the particular geniuses of Egyptian art that it could unite apparently disparate elements into a successful whole. The sculpture is in perfect condition except for the right side of the head of the uraeus and a few chips knocked from the edge of the base.

From Saqqara, late Twenty-sixth Dynasty, dark grey greywacke, length of base 104 cm., height of base 12 cm., width of base 29 cm., height of cow to horns 84 cm., height of Psamtik 44.5 cm.

BIBLIOGRAPHY: *PM* III, p. 178 (and map p. 174); *Tel*, pls. 174–5; Bothmer, *ESLP*, pp. 64, 68, 103.

COMMENTS: The Eighteenth Dynasty prototype is *J. d'E.* 38574 (Lange and Hirmer, *Egypt*, pls. 146, 147). The sculpture of Psamtik was found in a pit at Saqqara with two other statues dedicated by him, both of which are again in almost perfect condition: an Osiris (*Cat. gén.* 38358) and an Isis (*Cat. gén.* 38884). Bothmer, *ESLP*, no. 55, ascribes the head of another goddess to the same source. The pit contained later objects (see *PM* III, p. 178 and *ESLP*, no. 55). It is unlikely that such monumental sculptures as these of Psamtik were meant to be placed in a tomb, especially in a period when tomb sculpture was rare. All the monuments of Psamtik are more likely to have been temple donations, later removed for unknown reasons.

The treatment of Psamtik's face is very close to that of a head of Amasis in the University Museum, Philadelphia (*ESLP*, no. 53, with references to other sculptures of Amasis), except that the eyes of the king have a more sensuous outline. An earlier version of the tripartite torso is *Cat. gén.* 895 (*ESLP*, no. 52 B). Bothmer, *ESLP*, p. 64, dates Psamtik's figure toward the end of the reign of Amasis.

A similar large figure of the cow of Hathor is *Cat. gén.* 676 from the Delta (in *Journal d'Entrée* stated to be from Tell Abu Yasin; Borchardt, *Statuen*, gives Tell Timai as the source). Unfortunately, the figure of a kneeling man in front of the cow is completely lost. The sculpture should be about the same date as that of Psamtik, to judge from the similarly rich modelling. The most famous animal sculpture of the Twenty-sixth Dynasty is the hippopotamus goddess Tueris (*Cat. gén.* 39145) dedicated to a daughter of Psamtik I (*Tel*, pl. 177).

E.L.B.T.

39 Psamtik-sa-Neith

Catalogue général 726

This remarkable sculpture has been acclaimed as the finest example of the portraiture which was introduced in the Persian Twenty-seventh Dynasty and which began a tradition of realistic portraits lasting for several hundred years. Realism of the early Saite Dynasty has been said to be formulaic. The bust of Mentuemhat (no. 37) is certainly, however, an example of a true likeness in the earlier part of the Late Period. Nevertheless, after the reign of Psamtik I there seems to be little or no attempt to portray veristic features. As in the case of the Kushite Twenty-fifth Dynasty, it was left to foreign conquerors, this time the Persians, to inspire a renewed concern for portraiture, a concern which lasted through the early years of the Roman domination.

Psamtik-sa-Neith, 'Head of All the King's Workmen in Gold and Silver', kneels on a thick base with rounded front. He wears a sleeved shirt with V-neck, under which lies another garment. Wrapped tightly under the breasts is a long outer cloak, the corners of which are folded over. He holds an inscribed naos containing a damaged image of the god Osiris, who wears the feathered *atef* crown.

It is the head and face that arrest the attention of the viewer. The sculptor spared no effort to create the image of a living personality. The structure of the eyes is entirely plastic, except for the curious relief ridge which completely outlines them. The flesh of the cheeks and chin is richly modelled. The rounded tip of the nose is another specific detail. The lips, modelled like coils of clay, turn up slightly as if smiling, but a little muscle at the corners pulls the upper lip downward very slightly. This detail adds a certain introspection to the smile. The mouth is sunk in the cheeks as if the man had lost his teeth. The fat breasts bulge over the edge of the cloak. Other points of interest include the curve of the thighs squatting on the kneeling legs, and the splayed toes which so obviously exert pressure against the base. The head is shaven, exposing every detail of the structure of the skull.

As a masterpiece of specific individuality, the portrait of Psamtik-sa-Neith was rarely surpassed in ancient Egypt. Like Mentuemhat's, the head is that of an older man. Nearly all the portraits of the Late Period depict old age, as do those of earlier times. The elderly face has spiritual and physical character; the unformed features of youth were suitable enough for the idealizing representation of man that the Egyptian preferred during most of his history. The complete absence of any texts that might explain the emotional and

philosophical background of the outburst of verism in the Twenty-seventh Dynasty and later is cause for great regret.

From Mit Rahineh (Memphis), Twenty-seventh Dynasty (about 500 BC), dark green greywacke, height 44.5 cm.

BIBLIOGRAPHY: *ESLP*, no. 65, with earlier references.

COMMENTS: The statue has been fully published by Bothmer, *ESLP*, no. 65. The form of the garment, which appears for the first time in the Persian Period, is explained in *ESLP*, pp. 75–6. Its appearance in relief is seen in *ESLP*, no. 74. The peculiar sleeves of the jacket are also characteristic of the Twenty-seventh Dynasty. For the reintroduction of portraiture in the Twenty-seventh Dynasty, and its lasting effects, see *ESLP*, pp. 67 ff.

E.L.B.T.

40 Relief of Nefer-seshem-Psamtik

Journal d'Entrée 10978

The Thirtieth Dynasty forms the last phase of purely pharaonic art. An ephemeral Persian Thirty-first Dynasty was followed by the Macedonian conquest and the Ptolemaic Period. This is not to say that the Egyptians did not continue to produce fine sculpture: indeed some of the most brilliant portraits of ancient Egypt were executed under the Ptolemies. Nevertheless, the Thirtieth Dynasty is the last time that the Egyptians deliberately sought models from earlier work, and the sculptors of the period appear to have looked principally to the great renaissance of the early Twenty-sixth Dynasty for inspiration.

During the fourth century there were made a number of unusual reliefs, most of them with a torus moulding at the top, which used to be called 'neo-Memphite'. They were then thought to have been imitating Memphite work of the Old Kingdom. It is now clear that the term is a misnomer for more than one reason: many of the reliefs are not from Memphis at all, and their models are not, in fact, from the Old Kingdom. A detail of the present relief may be cited: the wigs of most of the women are cut upward from the back of the neck, a feature invented in the late Eighteenth Dynasty.

The relief of Nefer-seshem-Psamtik shows the owner seated at the left, facing right, in a chair the legs of which are fashioned in the form of a bull's legs. The chair stands on a rush mat set on edge (*cf.* the similar mannerism of no. 28), and the support of the seat ends in a papyrus flower. Nefer-seshem-Psamtik holds a long staff in his left hand and a folded kerchief in the right. He wears only a short pleated kilt and a broad collar. His hair or wig is of the baggy type.

A kneeling or squatting man is taking a brush from his palette. Set before him is his scribe's equipment: a bound mat on which are placed an ink or water pot and two rolls of papyrus tied together. The inscription above him labels the man as the 'Scribe of Gold'. The hieroglyphic sign for gold (*nbw*, 𓋞) is itself a collar with pendants and ties. The next group consists of a man holding what may be a papyrus roll and grasping a collar held out by a woman who holds a bracelet in her left hand. Two more groups of two women fill out the lintel, each woman carrying collars, counterpoises, or bracelets. Above each group is an inscription which states 'Presenting the Gold'. The women wear long gowns held by knotted shoulder straps, exposing one breast. Their ears appear to be adorned with rings attached to the tip of the ear; the lobes are notched, another late New Kingdom detail.

Earlier versions of this subject illustrate male artisans producing and presenting jewellery for the funerary equipment of the deceased. The presentation of gold to favoured courtiers was a custom of the New Kingdom, but the recipients were always high officials. The piling of jewellery near the figure of Nefer-seshem-Psamtik indicates clearly that the jewellery is being brought to him. The use of women for what was a traditionally male occupation is one more indication of the inventiveness of the Late Period artists. The characteristic orientation occurs again: the deceased faces right to observe the activities.

From Mit Rahineh (Memphis), Kom el Fakhri outside the temenos of the Temple of Ptah, Thirtieth Dynasty (about 360–350 BC), limestone, length 133 cm.

BIBLIOGRAPHY: *PM* III, p. 224; *Tel*, pl. 191; *5000 Years Catalogue*, London, pl. XXIII; *cf.* Yoyotte, *Chron. d'Eg.* 29 (1954) 278 ff.

COMMENTS: For the orientation of the scene *cf.* no. 5 and the order of events in the papyrus no. 35. In nos. 25 and 30, the scribes hold their papyrus rolls in the left hand, unrolling them from right to left. The richly plastic style of these reliefs has been ascribed incorrectly to Greek influence (*cf.* W. S. Smith, *Ancient Egypt*, 1960, p. 178). The sixth-century head of Psamtik (no. 38) is enough to show the purely Egyptian origin of the facial forms. The deep navels and surrounding pear-shaped abdominal flesh may also be compared with the similar structure of Psamtik's abdomen. It is, nevertheless, of great importance to recognize the enormous change that has occurred between the Fifth Dynasty relief of boatmen (no. 11) and the Ramesside dancers (no. 33) and Nefer-seshem-Psamtik's relief. In the early examples the quality of the relief is defined not so much by sculpture as it is by line, principally the outline itself which controls the forms of the relief. In the fourth century lintel, the outline is still important (it was never lost sight of in Egypt), but now the internal modelling has a far greater sculptural significance than it had had in earlier times. As a rule, Egyptian reliefs had been so anti-plastic, as it were, that it has been the habit of Egyptologists to use line-drawings in publishing them (a practice, it must be said, which does some injustice to the style). Such could not be done here. On the other hand, Nefer-seshem-Psamtik's relief must be compared with those of Hesy-Ra (no. 4) and Khai-bau-Sokar (no. 5) which, made at the beginning of the Old Kingdom, illustrate almost as great an inner plasticity as the much later example. Interestingly, the Egyptian artists rejected the boldness of the archaic reliefs and soon after created an almost paper-thin relief (*cf.* relief of Hemiunu, in Boston, W. S. Smith, *Ancient Egypt*, 1960, fig. 20).

The coiffure of the women is similar but not identical (with variations due to the elaborate ornament) to that of the lady harpist on a relief in Cleveland (*ESLP*, fig. 203). For these lintels in general, *cf. ESLP*, nos. 74, 82, 87, 88; Smith, *Art and Architecture*, p. 251 and n. 60 on p. 287, where it is conclusively shown that the reliefs are lintels over the doorways of small rooms, presumably tomb chambers. Although some of the reliefs have a Heliopolitan origin (*cf. ESLP*, *ibid.*, and Yoyotte, *Chron. d'Eg.* 29 [1954] 278–80), others have been found elsewhere in Lower Egypt, including the Delta. The facial types of Nefer-seshem-Psamtik's relief are very close to those of a lintel in The Walters Art Gallery, Baltimore (*ESLP*, no. 87, figs. 214–18), where the double fold under the chin is also found. Bothmer, *ibid.*, dates the Baltimore fragment to 350 BC and the Cleveland relief (*ESLP*, no. 82) to 365–360 BC. For the series of these reliefs in the Egyptian Museum, see *Le Musée égyptien*, 2, part 2 (1906) 74 ff. and pls. XXXII–XLII.

E.L.B.T.

41 Hor-si-Hor

Catalogue général 697

On the eve of the Roman domination, the sculptors of Ptolemaic Egypt produced a large series of remarkably life-like portraits. Always attributed in the past to Greek influence, we have seen even in the very brief survey of this exhibition that amongst the Egyptians themselves there was a living tradition of verism as strong as any in the Hellenistic world outside. Furthermore, the Ptolemies, at first alien rulers, were completely Egyptianized by the first century BC. Nevertheless, credit must be given to the intellectual climate of the times which permitted the Egyptian tradition to flourish in a world-wide atmosphere of sympathy to the representation of actuality. One of the great masterpieces of the period is the upper part of a statue of a man named Hor, a priest of the old god of scribes and writing Thoth. Hor's name is compounded with the expression *si-Hor*, 'son of Hor', referring either to his father, another Hor, or to the god Horus, in which case we have one of those theophoric names of which the Egyptians were so fond.

A little under life-size, the statue represents Hor-si-Hor in early middle age, standing with the left foot forward as usual. The mouth is lined with deep nasolabial grooves and sharp lines descend vertically from the corners of the lips. A determined chin juts forward sharply, continuing the line of the strong jawbones. The nose is large and heavy. Furrows are carved under the high and projecting cheek bones. The eyes are large and unusually wide open; asymmetrically, the left eye is smaller than the right. The brows are sharply modelled and emphasize the depth of the sockets. The upper lids, thick rolls of skin, are in relief, while the lower lids are modelled only. The upper lid extends beyond the lower slightly and ends in a point imbedded in the flesh of the socket. The hair recedes around the temples, but comes forward in a rounded widow's peak. The hair is arranged in impressionistically carved curls, perhaps the most specifically Hellenistic feature of the head and the series to which it belongs. The curls outlining the face appear to be brushed back from it. The ears lie naturally against the jaw bone and hair, and the tense muscles of the neck are carefully modelled. The V-shaped groove on the otherwise smooth forehead seems to be an accidental blemish.

The clothing is characteristic of statues of this type. A high, round-necked, short-sleeved shirt, a long skirt, and a serrated scarf or short cloak make up the costume. Here the hems of the neck and serrations of the shawl or cloak are in relief. Elaborately carved folds have a superficially Hellenistic appearance, but

: descendants of costumes like that of Psamtik-sa-Neith (no. 39), which, in other examples
ı Period, have varying degrees of folds and pleats under the breast. The serrations and folds
: back of Hor-si-Hor's statue as well as in front. A notable feature of this and many other
culptures is that the head turns slightly to the left. It has been observed above that the left eye
n and shaped differently from the right. At present, there is nothing to explain this curious

›-Hellenistic features of coiffure, costume and modelling of the face are organized within a
'hich is strictly Egyptian. The plasticity of the modelling is found some thousands of years

earlier (*cf. e.g.* nos. 4, 5, 7, 18, 31). The verism of the portraiture is perhaps more specific but no more telling than that of as idealizing a sculpture as Seneb's of the Sixth Dynasty (no. 12). The style of Egyptian sculpture has not changed, only some mannerisms have been introduced to highlight its intrinsic qualities.

From Alexandria, Kom el Damas, *c.* 50–30 BC, dark grey basalt or dioritic basalt, height 83 cm.

BIBLIOGRAPHY: *PM* IV, p. 4; *Tel*, pls. 217–18; Kunsthaus Zürich, *Koptische Kunst: Christentum am Nil* (exhibition November 1963–January 1964; also Essen previously), no. 11 and pl.; P. Graindor, *Les Bustes et Statues-Portraits Romains*, no. 70, pls. LXV–LXVI.

COMMENTS: For the costume see Bothmer, *ESLP*, pp. 178–9 with references to other studies. Pleats and folds are known in Egyptian sculpture from much earlier times, but the Late Period ancestors of the form as found on Hor-si-Hor's statue begin with such naturalistically treated folds as Brooklyn 37.353 (*ESLP*, figs. 151–2), a statue dated specifically to the Twenty-seventh Dynasty. Hor-si-Hor's statue is the masterpiece of a series including Detroit Institute of Arts 51.83 (*ESLP*, figs. 340–41, 343, a version produced or at least found in Upper Egypt). For a discussion of the group, see *ESLP*, nos. 131–2, 136.

Other more or less complete sculptures in the group include *Cat. gén.* 27495 (Graindor, no. 72), Cairo 2–3/25–9 (Graindor, no. 73), Alexandria 3192 (Graindor, no. 65), *Cat. gén.* 696 (Graindor, no. 66), *Cat. gén.* 1190 (Graindor, no. 68, seated), *J. d'E.* 33266 (Graindor, no. 70, standing carrying a naos). Several of the finest portraits of the period come from this group, including our no. 42, Brooklyn 58.30 (*ESLP*, no. 132), Alexandria 3204 (*ESLP*, no. 131), Boston 64.1468 (*The Connoisseur*, October 1968, p. 121, fig. 9; also *Ars Antiqua, Antike Kunstwerke, Auktion* I, Sale Catalogue, Lucerne, 2 May 1959, no. 10, pls. 4, 5). The latter head, probably a generation earlier than the statue of Hor-si-Hor, is a good example of its immediate predecessors.

The hair of Alexandria 3204 (*ESLP*, no. 131) is treated like that of Hor-si-Hor, but the curls of the former are rather more mechanical. The trapezoidal top of the back pillar with sloping top is common to a good many of the sculptures of the first century BC, but *cf.* the triangular top of no. 42. For Hor-si-Hor's inscriptions, see Daressy, *Rec. de trav.* 15 (1893) 157 f., no. 6, and remarks by Graindor, no. 70.

E.L.B.T.

42 A Frowning Man with Laurel-wreath Diadem

Journal d'Entrée 65424A

Under the Ptolemies the Egyptian aristocracy adhered to tradition in many ways, no doubt because the Ptolemies themselves had soon become an Egyptianized house. However, the chic Egyptian official occasionally affected the fashions of the busy Mediterranean world of which his country was now a part. Such a case is that of the small head exhibited here, adorned with a laurel wreath of purely Hellenistic origin. Yet, the new fashion had ancient prototypes in Egypt itself where the floral diadem was by no means unknown as early as the beginning of the Old Kingdom, and it is the form only that has been changed.

The sculpture is a remarkable exercise in the rendering of a face worn by worry and anxiety. It is not necessarily an old man who is shown: youths in their twenties may show such anxiety as is represented here. The man is endowed with a full head of Hellenistic curls—thick, full locks of hair radiating from the crown. Incised throughout, each lock a separate element (*cf.* the baboon's mane, no. 29), the curls are combed forward on the forehead where they are cut evenly without losing a sense of the separate locks. A further touch of reality is given by the curls which curve down over the temples.

The furrows of the forehead are utterly symmetrical. The lines of the face are equally balanced on each side. While it is true that the worried brow of a man does usually show an almost mechanical parallelism of furrows, here there is no sign of that tiny blemish or two that distinguishes the living flesh. Yet the abruptly hooked nose, with its flaring nostrils emphasized by sharply incised lines, is a feature that gives a strong impression of having been observed from the model in the studio.

The upper lids are large and hooded, their roots sinking deeply into the fleshy brows. The lower lids are barely indicated. The arched brows are free of any indication of hair: only the gnarled flesh is shown. Pouches of skin hang under the high, protruding cheek bones. The sunken cheeks are lined with ropey folds of skin. The nasolabial lines meet the bunched skin of the cheeks to form a frame around the mouth and chin. The sharply defined nose gives a hint of a stern, unyielding, perhaps even cruel character unsoftened by the sensuous lips. The haggard face is that of a man under great strain and such features in Egyptian art always represent men of some age. Yet there is something almost youthful in the head; perhaps it must be ascribed to the fact that the artist worked too hard to build veristic details within such a mechanical framework of symmetry.

Found with the head was a fragment of the lower part of the body. The figure was standing and wore a shawl or cloak in which the right side was pulled over the left (as in nearly every case of this kind of garment). The edge of the shawl is vertical and is serrated like that of no. 41, but the serrations here are fringed in a manner imitating the hair.

From Tell Umm el-Breigat (ancient Tebtunis) in the Fayum, *c.* 50–30 BC, limestone, height 8.5 cm.

BIBLIOGRAPHY: Exhibited in Japan, 1963, and illustrated as no. 11 of this catalogue in Japanese. Also illustrated in *5000 Years Catalogue*, Essen, no. 259.

COMMENTS: From 1930 to 1935 an Italian mission made some excavations at Tebtunis of which short preliminary reports have appeared, *ASAE* 31 (1931) 19 ff. and *Chron. d'Eg.* 13–14 (1932) 85 ff. (*cf. PM* IV, p. 103 for architecture and other references). In the first season of 1930–31 there was found an overlife-size limestone statue of a Ptolemaic king attired in traditional garb of *shendyt* kilt and *nemes* crown (Cairo *J. d'E.* 55960 now in Graeco-Roman Museum, Alexandria). The face has a grimacing mouth, furrowed brow, and hooked nose, and has been identified as Ptolemy XII (80–51 BC) on the basis of coin portraits, *cf.* Bothmer, *ESLP*, p. 171. Between the discovery of the royal statue and the small limestone head (1935), an inscription of Ptolemy XII was found, but in what context is not made clear.
There are some similarities that bring the Tebtunis head close to the major group of portraits of the period, including the so-called 'Black Head' of Brooklyn (58.30, *ESLP*, no. 132). In the latter, an over life-size head of diorite, the brows are completely plastic, the upper lids are deep and hooded, the nasolabial furrows encircle the mouth. And, like both nos. 41 and 42, the jaw of the Brooklyn head juts forward with a deep indentation between chin and lower lip. A notable difference between the hard stone examples just cited and the limestone head is that asymmetry is an essential characteristic of the former. The more tractable material, limestone, which theoretically might have permitted the sculptor even greater latitude in representing the peculiarities of an individual, in fact is used more conservatively in this regard. On the other hand, the softer material is clearly responsible for the extraordinary plasticity of the sculpture itself.

Floral diadems of traditional Egyptian form may be seen in the relief from Bersha of the Twelfth Dynasty (no. 15, with references) and the sculpture of the wife of Nakht-Min of the late Eighteenth Dynasty (no. 31).

E.L.B.T.

43 Bust of a Roman Caesar

Catalogue général 7257

With this imperious portrait of one of the Caesars of the late Roman empire, we reach the end of the ancient world and at the same time come full circle from the archaic statue (no. 2) made some 3,000 years earlier. Both sculptures are executed as abstractions of reality—the one is on the threshhold of realism as it was known in ancient Egypt; the other brings Egyptian realism to a close. Referring to the abstract quality of the Roman portrait, a classical archaeologist has described it as being in a 'cubist' style. From the Egyptian point of view, we may say that the designation is particularly apt in defining a sculpture that lies at the end of 3,000 years of cubism. True, the head of the Roman twists on its axis—the characteristic of so many post-fifth century BC sculptures executed by the Greeks and their followers—but the abstraction of the eyes and other facial features and the cubic shape of the head remind us of the quality *par excellence* of Egyptian sculpture: the fidelity with which the Egyptian artist followed the form of the blocks of stone from which he produced his statues.

The great portraits of the middle of the first century BC had a clear and definite role to play in the development of the veristic art of Rome of the late Republican and Augustan periods. From the third and fourth centuries AD comes a series of equally important documents in the idiom of an oriental world distracted by ideological and political schism. It is instructive to note, even if this is not the place for discussion of it, that much of the world's greatest art has been produced in times of strife and conflict. The conclusion of the battles that won the unification of Egypt about 3000 BC resulted in the unparalleled palette of Narmer (*cf.* no. 1). The dissolution of the Old Kingdom and the wars of Thebes for supremacy in Egypt produced the remarkable art of the Eleventh Dynasty. The conflict with the Hyksos brought forth the splendid monuments of the Seventeenth and early Eighteenth Dynasties. The break-up of the oriental world of the first century BC has given us the magnificent portraits of Egypt and Rome; and we can cite the more recent example of the art of the Italian Renaissance, an art created in the midst of almost continuous warfare. The implications of these observations on the art of the past cannot be discussed here in terms of today's art.

The tetrarchy, a futile attempt to hold the Empire together by dividing authority between Augusti and Caesars in the various regions, fell apart at the beginning of the fourth century. In 296 Alexandria revolted;

and about the same time other imperial centres rose against the Roman domination. In each area strong-willed military leaders were put in charge. One of these was a certain Maximinus Daia, who ruled from Alexandria as Caesar under the Augustus Galerius from 306 to 309. Later Maximinus himself was an Augustus until 313, and it is possible that the portrait here is of him, although Licinius has also been put forward as a candidate.

The surviving porphyry portraits of these eastern rulers reveal men of severe and uncompromising character. Their militarism is inherent in the brutal strength of their sculptures. Their oriental flavour is underlined by the large, wide-open eyes; eyes which appear to be involved in the mysticism of cults as widely separated as those of Isis, Christianity, and Syrian sun-worship. They are eyes which look beyond the rationalism of the Hellenistic world; eyes which turn back to those beliefs in other-worldly manifestations known in ancient Egypt. The pupils and irises form double button-holes cut in very high relief, and the lids are simply outlines of equally high relief. The asymmetry of the eyes fits well with the contorted, frowning brows over which the hair of the brows arches sensuously.

Outside of the rigid furrows of the forehead, the planes of the face are not modelled: everything conforms to the cuboid form of the head. Even the relief eyes are severe abstractions of this cubism. The beard and moustache are indicated by pointing only. In good Egyptian tradition, the hair line is formed in low relief around the forehead; the hair itself is again pointed with the tool. Another reference to pre-Roman Egypt is the tab of hair descending in front of each ear. The general's cloak, modelled in richly abstract folds, is caught on the right shoulder by a fibula.

From Benha (ancient Athribis), about AD 310, imperial porphyry, height 57 cm.

BIBLIOGRAPHY: R. Delbrueck, *Spätantike Porphyrwerke*, pp. 92 ff., pls. 38, 39; G. Duthuit, *La Sculpture Copte*, pp. 30 f.; H. P. l'Orange, *Studien zur Geschichte des spätantiken Porträts*, pp. 22 f.; P. Graindor, *Bustes et Statues-Portraits Romains*, no. 23 and pl. XXI; *Tel*, pls. 222–3; *5000 Years Catalogue*, London, pl. XXXVII; C. C. Vermeule, *JARCE* 1 (1962) 63 ff., pl. VII, 3; Kodansha, pl. 91 (colour).

COMMENTS: A very useful discussion of late Roman portraiture from Egypt and the east is found in C. C. Vermeule, 'Egyptian Contributions to Late Roman Imperial Portraiture', *JARCE* 1 (1962) 63 ff., pls. VI–X. The closest parallels in style to the Athribis head are the well-known porphyry tetrarchal sculptures of Diocletianus and Maximianus Augusti at San Marco, Venice (Vermeule, pl. VII, 4) and at Rome (Vatican Library, Vermeule, pl. VII, 5). The staring, mystical eyes which herald medieval Christian art are found in approximately contemporary mummy paintings and pseudo-sculptures from Egypt, such as the painted stucco mask in Boston (W. S. Smith, *Ancient Egypt*, 1960, fig. 131), a similar mask in the Brooklyn Museum (J. Cooney, *Five Years of Collecting Egyptian Art*, pl. 92), and a painting on wood (Cooney, frontispiece). For such portraits in general, with further parallels, see K. Parlasca, *Mumienportäts und verwandte Denkmäler*. For the purplish-red stone called 'imperial' porphyry see Lucas, pp. 416–18; R. Engelbach, *ASAE* 31 (1931) 137 ff. with map and pls. II–III.

E.L.B.T.